OLD MOⓞ

HOROSCOPE AND ASTRAL DIARY

VIRGO

foulsham
LONDON • NEW YORK • TORONTO • SYDNEY

W. Foulsham & Co. Ltd
for Foulsham Publishing Ltd
The Old Barrel Store, Drayman's Lane, Marlow, Bucks SL7 2FF

Foulsham books can be found in all good bookshops and direct from
www.foulsham.com

ISBN: 978-0-572-04642-2

Copyright © 2016 Foulsham Publishing Ltd

A CIP record for this book is available from the British Library

Printed in Denmark by Nørhaven, Viborg

CONTENTS

INTRODUCTION

Astrology has been a part of life for centuries now, and no matter how technological our lives become, it seems that it never diminishes in popularity. For thousands of years people have been gazing up at the star-clad heavens and seeing their own activities and proclivities reflected in the movement of those little points of light. Across centuries countless hours have been spent studying the way our natures, activities and decisions seem to be paralleled by their predictable movements. Old Moore, a time-served veteran in astrological research, continues to monitor the zodiac and has produced the Astral Diary for 2017, tailor-made to your own astrological makeup.

Old Moore's Astral Diary is unique in its ability to get the heart of your nature and to offer you the sort of advice that might come from a trusted friend. It enables you to see in a day-by-day sense exactly how the planets are working for you. The diary section advises how you can get the best from upcoming situations and allows you to plan ahead successfully. There's also room on each daily entry to record your own observations or appointments.

While other popular astrology books merely deal with your astrological 'Sun sign', the Astral Diaries go much further. Every person on the planet is unique and Old Moore allows you to access your individuality in a number of ways. The front section gives you the chance to work out the placement of the Moon at the time of your birth and to see how its position has set an important seal on your overall nature. Perhaps most important of all, you can use the Astral Diary to discover your Rising Sign. This is the zodiac sign that was appearing over the Eastern horizon at the time of your birth and is just as important to you as an individual as is your Sun sign.

It is the synthesis of many different astrological possibilities that makes you what you are and with the Astral Diaries you can learn so much. How do you react to love and romance? Through the unique Venus tables and the readings that follow them, you can learn where the planet Venus was at the time of your birth. It is even possible to register when little Mercury is 'retrograde', which means that it appears to be moving backwards in space when viewed from the Earth. Mercury rules communication, so be prepared to deal with a few setbacks in this area when you see the sign ☿. The Astral Diary will be an interest and a support throughout the whole year ahead.

Old Moore extends his customary greeting to all people of the Earth and offers his age-old wishes for a happy and prosperous period ahead.

THE ESSENCE
OF VIRGO

Exploring the Personality of
Virgo the Virgin

(24TH AUGUST – 24TH SEPTEMBER)

What's in a sign?

Virgo people tend to be a rather extraordinary sort of mixture. Your ruling planet is Mercury, which makes you inclined to be rather chatty and quite sociable. On the other hand, yours is known as an Earth-ruled zodiac sign, which is usually steady and sometimes quite reserved. Thus, from the start, there are opposing energies ruling your life. This is not a problem when the right sort of balance is achieved and that is what you are looking for all the time. Repressed social and personal communication can make you worrisome, which in turn leads to a slightly fussy tendency that is not your most endearing quality.

At best you are quite ingenious and can usually rely on your strong intuition when weighing up the pros and cons of any given situation. Like all Earth signs you are able to accrue wealth and work hard to achieve your ultimate objectives in life. However, one is left with the impression that problems arise for Virgo when acquisition takes over. In other words you need to relax more and to enjoy the fruits of your successes on a more regular basis.

Tidiness is important to you, and not just around your home. You particularly don't like loose ends and can be meticulous in your sense of detail. It seems likely that the fictional Sherlock Holmes was a Virgo subject and his ability to get to the absolute root of all situations is a stock-in-trade for the sign of the Virgin. Flexibility is especially important in relationships and you shouldn't become so obsessed with the way surroundings look that you fail to make the most of social opportunities.

Another tendency for Virgo is a need to 'keep up with the Joneses'. Why do you do this? Mainly because like your fellow Mercury-ruled sign of Gemini you haven't really as much confidence as seems to be the case. As a result you want to know that you are as good as anyone else, and if possible better. This can, on occasion, lead to a sort of subconscious race that you can never hope to win. Learn to relax, and to recognise when you are on top anyway, and you are really motoring.

Virgo resources

Virgoan people are not at all short of savvy, and one of the most important considerations about your make-up is that you usually know how to proceed in a practical sense. At your disposal you have an armoury of weapons that can lead to a successful sort of life, especially in a practical and financial sense.

Your ruling planet, Mercury, makes you a good communicator and shows you the way to get on-side with the world at large. This quality means that you are rarely short of the right sort of information that is necessary in order to get things right first time. Where this doesn't prove to be possible you have Earth-sign tenacity, and an ability to work extremely hard for long hours in order to achieve your intended objectives. On the way you tend on the whole to make friends, though you might find it hard to get through life without picking up one or two adversaries too.

Virgo people are capable of being gregarious and gossipy, whilst at the same time retaining an internal discipline which more perceptive people are inclined to recognise instinctively. You cement secure friendships and that means nearly always having someone to rely on in times of difficulty. But this isn't a one-way street, because you are a very supportive type yourself and would fight tenaciously on behalf of a person or a cause that you supported wholeheartedly. At such times you can appear to be quite brave, even though you could be quaking inside.

A tendency towards being nervy is not always as evident as you might think, mainly because you have the power and ability to keep it behind closed doors. Retaining the secrets of friends, despite your tendency to indulge in gossip, is an important part of your character and is the reason that others learn to trust you. Organisational skills are good and you love to sort out the puzzles of life, which makes you ideal for tedious jobs that many other people would find impossible to complete. Your curiosity knows no bounds and you would go to almost any length to answer questions that are uppermost in your mind at any point in time.

Beneath the surface

So what are you really like? Well, in the case of Virgo this might be the most interesting journey of all, and one that could deeply surprise even some of those people who think they know you very well indeed. First of all it must be remembered that your ruling planet is Mercury, known as the lord of communication. As a result it's important for you to keep in touch with the world at large. That's fine, except for the fact that your Earth-sign tendencies are inclined to make you basically quiet by nature.

Here we find something of a contradiction and one that leads to more than a few misunderstandings. You are particularly sensitive to little changes out there in the cosmos and so can be much more voluble on some days than on others. The result can be that others see you as being somewhat moody, which isn't really the case at all.

You are inclined to be fairly nervy and would rarely be quite as confident as you give the impression of being. Although usually robust in terms of general health, this doesn't always seem to be the case and a tendency towards a slightly hypochondriac nature can be the result. Some Virgoans can make an art form out of believing that they are unwell and you need to understand that part of the reason for this lies in your desire for attention.

Another accusation that is levelled at Virgoans is that they are inclined to be fussy over details. This is also an expression of your lack of basic confidence in yourself. For some reason you subconsciously assume that if every last matter is dealt with absolutely, all will work out well. In reality the more relaxed you remain, the better you find your ability to cope with everyday life.

The simple truth is that you are much more capable than your inner nature tends to believe and could easily think more of yourself than you do. You have a logical mind, but also gain from the intuition that is possessed by all Mercury-ruled individuals. The more instinctive you become, the less you worry about things and the more relaxed life can seem to be. You also need to override a natural suspicion of those around you. Trust is a hard thing for you, but a very important one.

Making the best of yourself

There are many ways in which you can exploit the best potentials of your zodiac sign, and at the same time play down some of the less favourable possibilities. From the very start it's important to realise that the main criticism that comes your way from the outside world is that you are too fussy by half. So, simply avoid being critical of others and the way they do things. By all means stick to your own opinions, but avoid forcing them onto other people. If you can get over this hurdle, your personal popularity will already be that much greater. If people love you, you care for them in return – it's as simple as that, because at heart you aren't really very complicated.

Despite the fact that a little humility would go a long way, you also do need to remain sure of yourself. There's no real problem in allowing others their head, while following your own opinions all the same. Use your practical skills to the full and don't rush things just because other people seem to do so. Although you are ruled by quick Mercury you also come from an Earth sign, which means steady progress.

Find outlets to desensitise your over-nervy nature. You can do this with plenty of healthy exercise and by taking an interest in subject matter that isn't of any great importance, but which you find appealing all the same. Avoid concentrating too much on any one thing, because that is the road to paranoia.

Realise that you have an innate sense of what is right, and that if it is utilised in the right way you can make gains for yourself and for the people you love. You have a good fund of ideas, so don't be afraid to use them. Most important of all you need to remain confident but flexible. That's the path to popularity – something you need much more than you might realise.

The impressions you give

This can be something of a problem area to at least some people born under the zodiac sign of Virgo. There isn't much doubt that your heart is in the right place and this fact isn't lost on many observers. All the same, you can appear to be very definite in your opinions, in fact to the point of stubbornness, and you won't give ground when you know you are in the right. A slight problem here might be that Virgoans nearly always think they have the moral and legal high ground. In the majority of cases this may indeed be true, but there are ways and means of putting the message across.

What Virgo needs more than anything else is tact. A combination of Mercury, ruling your means of communication, and your Earth-sign heritage can, on occasions, make you appear to be rather blunt. Mercury also aids in quick thinking and problem solving. The sum total can make it appear that you don't take other people's opinions into account and that you are prepared to railroad your ideas through if necessary.

Most people recognise that you are very capable, and may therefore automatically turn to you for leadership. It isn't certain how you will react under any given circumstance because although you can criticise others, your Earth-sign proclivities don't make you a natural leader. In a strong supportive role you can be wonderful and it is towards this scenario that you might choose to look.

Avoid people accusing you of being fussy by deliberately cultivating flexibility in your thinking and your actions. You are one of the kindest and most capable people to be found anywhere in the zodiac. All you need to do to complete the picture is to let the world at large know what you are. With your natural kindness and your ability to get things done you can show yourself to be a really attractive individual. Look towards a brush-up of your public persona. Deep inside you are organised and caring, though a little nervy. Let people know exactly what you are – it only makes you more human.

The way forward

Before anyone can move forward into anything it is important for them to realise exactly where they are now. In your case this is especially true. Probably the most problematic area of Virgo is in realising not what is being done but rather why. It is the inability to ask this question on a regular basis that leads Virgo into a rut now and again. Habit isn't simply a word to many people born under the zodiac sign of Virgo, it's a religion. The strange thing about this fact is that if you find yourself catapulted, against your will, into a different sort of routine, you soon learn to adopt it as if it were second nature. In other words this way of behaving is endemic, but not necessarily inevitable. The way out of it is simple and comes thanks to your ruling planet of Mercury. Keep talking, and at the same time listen. Adapt your life on a regular basis and say 'So many habits are not necessary' at least ten times a day.

All the same it wouldn't be very prudent to throw out the baby with the bath water. Your ability to stick at things is justifiably legendary. This generally means that you arrive at your desired destination in life, even though it might take you a long time to get there. The usual result is respect from people who don't have your persistence or tenacity.

With regard to love and affection you are in a good position to place a protecting blanket around those you love the most. This is fine, as long as you check regularly that you are not suffocating them with it. If you allow a certain degree of freedom people will respect your concern all the more, and they won't fight against it. By all means communicate your affection and don't allow your natural Earth-sign reserve to get in the way of expressing feelings that are quite definite internally. This is another aspect of letting the world know what you are really like and is of crucial importance to your zodiac sign.

You need variety, and if possible an absence of worry. Only when things are going wrong do Virgoans become the fussy individuals that sometimes attract a little criticism. As long as you feel that you are in charge of your own destiny, you can remain optimistic – another vital requisite for Virgo. With just a little effort you can be one of the most popular and loved people around. Add to this your natural ability to succeed and the prognosis for the sign of the Virgin is very good.

VIRGO ON THE CUSP

O ld Moore is often asked how astrological profiles are altered for those people born at either the beginning or the end of a zodiac sign, or, more properly, on the cusps of a sign. In the case of Virgo this would be on the 24th of August and for two or three days after, and similarly at the end of the sign, probably from the 21st to the 23rd of September. In this year's Astral Diaries, once again, Old Moore sets out to explain the differences regarding cuspid signs.

The Leo Cusp – August 24th to 26th

If anything is designed to lighten the load of being a Virgoan, it's having a Leo quality in the nature too. All Virgoans are inclined to take themselves too seriously on occasions and they don't have half as much self-esteem as they could really use effectively. Being born on the Leo cusp gives better self-confidence, less of the supreme depths which Virgo alone can display and a much more superficial view of many aspects of life. The material success for which Virgo is famous probably won't be lacking, but there will also be a determination to have fun and let the bright, aspiring qualities that are so popular in the Leo character show.

In matters of love, you are likely to be easy-going, bright, bubbly and always willing to have a laugh. You relish good company, and though you sometimes go at things like a bull at a gate, your intentions are true and you know how to get others to like you a great deal. Family matters are right up your street, because not only do you have the ability to put down firm and enduring roots, but you are the most staunch and loyal protector of family values that anyone could wish for.

When it comes to working, you seem to have the best combination of all. You have the ability to work long and hard, achieving your objectives as all Virgoans do, but managing to do so with a smile permanently fixed to your face. You are naturally likely to find yourself at the head of things, where your combination of skills is going to be of the greatest use. This sign combination is to be found in every nook and cranny of the working world but perhaps less frequently in jobs which involve getting your hands dirty.

There are times when you definitely live on your nerves and when you don't get the genuine relaxation that the Virgoan qualities within you demand. Chances are you are much more robust than you consider yourself to be, and as long as you keep busy most of the time you tend to enjoy a contented life. The balance usually works well, because Leo lifts Virgo, whilst Virgo stabilises an often too superficial Lion.

The Libra Cusp – September 21st to 23rd

Virgo responds well to input from other parts of the zodiac and probably never more so than in the case of the Libran cusp. The reasons for this are very simple: what Virgo on its own lacks, Libra possesses, and it's the same on the other side of the coin. Libra is often flighty and doesn't take enough time to rest, but it is compensated by the balance inherent in the sign, so it weighs things carefully. Virgo on the other hand is deep and sometimes dark, but because it's ruled by capricious little Mercury, it can also be rather too impetuous. The potential break-even point is obvious and usually leads to a fairly easy-going individual, who is intellectual, thoughtful and practical when necessary.

You are a great person to have around in good times and bad, and you know how to have fun. A staunch support and helper to your friends, you enjoy a high degree of popularity, which usually extends to affairs of the heart. There may be more than one of these in your life and it's best for people born on this cusp not to marry in haste or too early in life. But even if you get things wrong first time around, you have the ability to bounce back quickly and don't become easily discouraged. It is good for you to be often in the company of gregarious and interesting people, but you are quite capable of surviving on your own when you have to.

Health matters may be on your mind more than is strictly necessary, and it's true that you can sometimes worry yourself into minor ailments that would not otherwise have existed. It is important for you to get plenty of rest and also to enjoy yourself. The more you work on behalf of others, the less time you spend thinking about your own possible ailments. Anxiety needs to be avoided, often by getting to the root of a problem and solving it quickly.

A capable and committed worker, you are at your best when able to share the decisions, but you are quite reliable when you have to make up your mind alone. You would never bully those beneath you. You are never short of support and you bring joy to life most of the time.

VIRGO AND ITS ASCENDANTS

The nature of every individual on the planet is composed of the rich variety of zodiac signs and planetary positions that were present at the time of their birth. Your Sun sign, which in your case is Virgo, is one of the many factors when it comes to assessing the unique person you are. Probably the most important consideration, other than your Sun sign, is to establish the zodiac sign that was rising over the eastern horizon at the time that you were born. This is your Ascending or Rising sign. Most popular astrology fails to take account of the Ascendant, and yet its importance remains with you from the very moment of your birth, through every day of your life. The Ascendant is evident in the way you approach the world, and so, when meeting a person for the first time, it is this astrological influence that you are most likely to notice first. Our Ascending sign essentially represents what we appear to be, while the Sun sign is what we feel inside ourselves.

The Ascendant also has the potential for modifying our overall nature. For example, if you were born at a time of day when Virgo was passing over the eastern horizon (this would be around the time of dawn) then you would be classed as a double Virgo. As such, you would typify this zodiac sign, both internally and in your dealings with others. However, if your Ascendant sign turned out to be a Fire sign, such as Aries, there would be a profound alteration of nature, away from the expected qualities of Virgo.

One of the reasons why popular astrology often ignores the Ascendant is that it has always been rather difficult to establish. Old Moore has found a way to make this possible by devising an easy-to-use table, which you will find on page 125 of this book. Using this, you can establish your Ascendant sign at a glance. You will need to know your rough time of birth, then it is simply a case of following the instructions.

For those readers who have no idea of their time of birth it might be worth allowing a good friend, or perhaps your partner, to read through the section that follows this introduction. Someone who deals with you on a regular basis may easily discover your Ascending sign, even though you could have some difficulty establishing it for yourself. A good understanding of this component of your nature is essential if you want to be aware of that 'other person' who is responsible for the way you make contact with the world at large. Your Sun sign, Ascendant sign, and the other pointers in this book will, together, allow you a far better understanding of what makes you tick as an individual. Peeling back the different layers of your astrological make-up can be an enlightening experience, and the Ascendant may represent one of the most important layers of all.

Virgo with Virgo Ascendant

You get the best of both worlds, and on rare occasions the worst too. Frighteningly efficient, you have the ability to scare people with your constant knack of getting it right. This won't endear you to everyone, particularly those who pride themselves on being disorganised. You make a loyal friend and would do almost anything for someone who is important to you, though you do so in a quiet way because you are not the most noisy of types. Chances are that you possess the ability to write well and you also have a cultured means of verbal communication on those occasions when you really choose to speak out.

It isn't difficult for you to argue your case, though much of the time you refuse to do so and can lock yourself into your own private world for days on end. If you are at ease with yourself you possess a powerful personality, which you can express well. Conversely, you can live on your nerves and cause problems for yourself. Meditation is good, fussing over details that really don't matter at all is less useful. Once you have chosen a particular course of action there are few people around with sufficient will-power to prevent you from getting what you want. Wide open spaces where the hand of nature is all around can make you feel very relaxed.

Virgo with Libra Ascendant

Libra has the ability to lighten almost any load and it is particularly good at doing so when it is brought together with the much more repressed sign of Virgo. To the world at large you seem relaxed, happy and able to cope with most of the pressures that life places upon you. Not only do you deal with your own life in a bright and breezy manner but you are usually on hand to help others out of any dilemma that they might make for themselves. With excellent powers of communication you leave the world at large in no doubt whatsoever concerning both your opinions and your wishes. It is in the talking stakes that you really excel because Virgo brings the silver tongue of Mercury and Libra adds the Air-sign desire to be in constant touch with the world outside your door.

You like to have a good time and are often found in the company of interesting and stimulating people, who have the ability to bring out the very best in your bright and sparkling personality. Underneath however, there is still much of the worrying Virgoan to be found and this means that you have to learn to relax inside as well as appearing to do so externally. In fact you are much more complex than most people would realise and definitely would not be suited to a life that allowed you too much time to think about yourself.

Virgo with Scorpio Ascendant

This is intensity carried through to the absolute. If you have a problem it is that you fail to externalise all that is going on inside that deep, bubbling cauldron of your inner self. Realising what you are capable of is not a problem, these only start when you have to make it plain to those around you what you want. Part of the reason for this is that you don't always understand yourself. You love intensely and would do absolutely anything for a person you are fond of, even though you might have to inconvenience yourself a great deal on the way. Relationships can cause you slight problems however, since you need to associate with people who at least come somewhere near to understanding what makes you tick. If you manage to bridge the gap between yourself and the world that constantly knocks on your door, you show yourself to be powerful, magnetic and compulsive.

There are times when you definitely prefer to stay quiet though you do have a powerful ability to get your message across when you think it is necessary to do so. There are people around who might think that you are a push-over but they could easily get a shock when you sense that the time is right to answer back. You probably have a very orderly house and don't care for clutter of any sort.

Virgo with Sagittarius Ascendant

This is a combination that might look rather odd at first sight because these two signs have so very little in common. However the saying goes that opposites attract and in terms of the personality you display to the world this is especially true in your case. Not everyone understands what makes you tick but you try to show the least complicated face to the world that you can manage to display. You can be deep and secretive on occasions, and yet at other times you can start talking as soon as you climb out of bed and never stop until you are back there again. Inspirational and spontaneous, you take the world by storm on those occasions when you are free from worries and firing on all cylinders. It is a fact that you support your friends, though there are rather more of them than would be the case for Virgo taken on its own and you don't always choose them as wisely as you might.

There are times when you display a temper and although Sagittarius is incapable of bearing a grudge, the same cannot be said for Virgo, which has a better memory than the elephant. For the best results in life you need to relax as much as possible and avoid overheating that powerful and busy brain. Virgo gives you the ability to concentrate on one thing at once, a skill you should encourage.

Virgo with Capricorn Ascendant

Your endurance, persistence and concentration are legendary and there is virtually nothing that eludes you once you have the bit between your teeth. You are not the pushy, fussy, go-getting sort of Virgoan but are steady, methodical and very careful. Once you have made up your mind, a whole team of wild horses could not change it and although this can be a distinct blessing at times, it is a quality that can bring odd problems into your life too. The difficulty starts when you adopt a lost or less than sensible cause. Even in the face of overwhelming evidence that you are wrong there is something inside you that prevents any sort of U-turn and so you walk forward as solidly as only you are able, to a destination that won't suit you at all.

There are few people around who are more loyal and constant than you can be. There is a lighter and brighter side to your nature and the one or two people who are most important in your life will know how to bring it out. You have a wicked sense of humour, particularly if you have had a drink or when you are feeling on top form. Travel does you the world of good, even if there is a part of you that would rather stay at home. You have a potent, powerful and magnetic personality but for much of the time it is kept carefully hidden.

Virgo with Aquarius Ascendant

How could anyone make convention unconventional? Well, if anyone can manage, you can. There are great contradictions here because on the one hand you always want to do what is expected, but the Aquarian quality within your nature loves to surprise everyone on the way. If you don't always know what you are thinking or doing, it's a pretty safe bet that others won't either, so it's important on occasions to stop and really think. However this is not a pressing concern because you tend to live a fairly happy life and muddle through no matter what. Other people tend to take to you well and it is likely that you will have many friends. You tend to be bright and cheerful and can approach even difficult tasks with the certainty that you have the skills necessary to see them through to their conclusion. Give and take are important factors in the life of any individual and particularly so in your case. Because you can stretch yourself in order to understand what makes other people think and act in the way that they do, you have the reputation of being a good friend and a reliable colleague.

In love you can be somewhat more fickle than the typical Virgoan and yet you are always interesting to live with. Where you are, things happen, and you mix a sparkling wit with deep insights.

Virgo with Pisces Ascendant

You might have been accused on occasions of being too sensitive for your own good, a charge that is not entirely without foundation. Certainly you are very understanding of the needs of others, sometimes to the extent that you put everything aside to help them. This would also be true in the case of charities, for you care very much about the world and the people who cling tenaciously to its surface. Your ability to love on a one-to-one basis knows no bounds though you may not discriminate as much as you could, particularly when young, and might have one or two false starts in the love stakes. You don't always choose to verbalise your thoughts and this can cause problems, because there is always so much going on in your mind and Virgo especially needs good powers of communication. Pisces is quieter and you need to force yourself to say what you think when the explanation is important.

You would never betray a confidence and sometimes take on rather more for the sake of your friends than is strictly good for you. This is not a fault but can cause you problems all the same. Because you are so intuitive there is little that escapes your attention, though you should avoid being pessimistic about your insights. Changes of scenery suit you and extensive travel would bring out the best in what can be a repressed nature at times.

Virgo with Aries Ascendant

Virgo is steady and sure, though also fussy and stubborn. Aries is fast and determined, restless and active. It can be seen already that this is a rather strange meeting of characteristics and because Virgo is ruled by capricious Mercury, the result will change from hour to hour and day to day. It isn't merely that others find it difficult to know where they are with you; they can't even understand what makes you tick. This will make you the subject of endless fascination and attention, at which you will be apparently surprised but inwardly pleased. If anyone ever really gets to know what goes on in that busy mind they may find the implications very difficult to deal with and it is a fact that only you would have the ability to live inside your crowded head.

As a partner and a parent you are second to none, though you would tend to get on better with your children once they started to grow, since by this time you may be slightly less restricting to their own desires, which will often clash with your own on their behalf. You are capable of give and take and could certainly not be considered selfish, though your desire to get the best from everyone might be misconstrued on occasion.

Virgo with Taurus Ascendant

This combination tends to amplify the Taurean qualities that you naturally possess and this is the case because both Taurus and Virgo are Earth signs. However, there are certain factors related to Virgo that show themselves very differently than the sign's cousin Taurus. Virgo is more fussy, nervy and pedantic than Taurus and all of these qualities are going to show up in your nature at one level or another. On the plus side you might be slightly less concerned about having a perfect home and a perfect family, and your interest in life appears at a more direct level than that of the true Taurean. You care very much about your home and family and are very loyal to your friends. It's true that you sometimes tend to try and take them over and you can also show a marked tendency to dominate, but your heart is in the right place and most people recognise that your caring is genuine.

One problem is that there are very few shades of grey in your life, which is certainly not the case for other zodiac sign combinations. Living your life in the way that you do there isn't much room for compromise and this fact alone can prove to be something of a problem where relationships are concerned. In a personal sense you need a partner who is willing to be organised and one who relies on your judgements, which don't change all that often.

Virgo with Gemini Ascendant

A Gemini Ascendant means that you are ruled by Mercury, both through your Sun sign and through the sign that was rising at the time of your birth. This means that words are your basic tools in life and you use them to the full. Some writers have this combination, because even speaking to people virtually all the time is not enough. Although you have many friends you are fairly high-minded, which means that you can make enemies too. The fact is that people either care very much for you, or else they don't like you at all. This can be difficult for you to come to terms with because you don't really set out to cause friction – it simply attracts itself to you.

Although you love travel, home is important too and there is a basic insecurity in your nature that comes about as a result of an overdose of Mercury, which makes you nervy and sometimes far less confident than anyone would guess. Success in your life may be slower arriving with this combination because you are determined to achieve your objectives on your own terms and this can take time. Always a contradiction, often a puzzle to others, your ultimate happiness in life is directly proportional to the effort you put in, though this should not mean wearing yourself out on the way.

Virgo with Cancer Ascendant

What can this union of zodiac signs bring to the party that isn't there in either Virgo or Cancer alone? Well quite a bit actually. Virgo can be very fussy on occasions and too careful for its own good. The presence of steady, serene Cancer alters the perspectives and allows a smoother, more flowing Virgoan to greet the world. You are chatty, easy to know and exhibit a combination of the practical skills of Virgo, together with the deep and penetrating insights that are typical of Cancer. This can make you appear to be very powerful, and your insights are second to none. You are a born organiser and love to be where things are happening, even if you are only there to help make the sandwiches or to pour the tea. Invariably your role will be much greater but you don't seek personal acclaim and are a good team player on most occasions.

There is a quiet side to your nature and those who live with you will eventually get used to your need for solitude. This seems strange because Virgo is generally such a chatterbox and, taken on its own, is rarely quiet for long. In love you show great affection and a sense of responsibility that makes you an ideal parent, though it is possible sometimes that you care rather more than you are willing to show.

Virgo with Leo Ascendant

Here we have cheerfulness allied to efficiency, which can be a very positive combination most of the time. With all the sense of honour, justice and bravery of the Leo subject, Virgo adds staying power through tedious situations and offers you a slightly more serious view of life than we would expect from the Lion alone. In almost any situation you can keep going until you get to your chosen destination and you also find the time to reach out to the people who need your unique nature the most. Few would deny your kindness, though you can attract a little envy because it seems as though yours is the sort of personality that everyone else wants.

Most people born with this combination have a radiant smile and will do their best to think situations through carefully. If there is a tendency to be foolhardy, it is carefully masked beneath a covering of Virgoan common sense. Family matters are dealt with efficiently and with great love. Some might see you as close one moment and distant the next. The truth is that you are always on the go and have a thousand different things to think about, all at the same time. On the whole your presence is noticed and you may represent the most loyal friend of them all.

THE MOON AND THE PART IT PLAYS IN YOUR LIFE

In astrology the Moon is probably the single most important heavenly body after the Sun. Its unique position, as partner to the Earth on its journey around the solar system, means that the Moon appears to pass through the signs of the zodiac extremely quickly. The zodiac position of the Moon at the time of your birth plays a great part in personal character and is especially significant in the build-up of your emotional nature.

Sun Moon Cycles

The first lunar cycle deals with the part the position of the Moon plays relative to your Sun sign. I have made the fluctuations of this pattern easy for you to understand by means of a simple cyclic graph. It appears on the first page of each 'Your Month At A Glance', under the title 'Highs and Lows'. The graph displays the lunar cycle and you will soon learn to understand how its movements have a bearing on your level of energy and your abilities.

Your Own Moon Sign

Discovering the position of the Moon at the time of your birth has always been notoriously difficult because tracking the complex zodiac positions of the Moon is not easy. This process has been reduced to three simple stages with Old Moore's unique Lunar Tables. A breakdown of the Moon's zodiac positions can be found from page 28 onwards, so that once you know what your Moon Sign is, you can see what part this plays in the overall build-up of your personal character.

If you follow the instructions on the next page you will soon be able to work out exactly what zodiac sign the Moon occupied on the day that you were born and you can then go on to compare the reading for this position with those of your Sun sign and your Ascendant. It is partly the comparison between these three important positions that goes towards making you the unique individual you are.

24

HOW TO DISCOVER YOUR MOON SIGN

This is a three-stage process. You may need a pen and a piece of paper but if you follow the instructions below the process should only take a minute or so.

STAGE 1 First of all you need to know the Moon Age at the time of your birth. If you look at Moon Table 1, on page 26, you will find all the years between 1919 and 2017 down the left side. Find the year of your birth and then trace across to the right to the month of your birth. Where the two intersect you will find a number. This is the date of the New Moon in the month that you were born. You now need to count forward the number of days between the New Moon and your own birthday. For example, if the New Moon in the month of your birth was shown as being the 6th and you were born on the 20th, your Moon Age Day would be 14. If the New Moon in the month of your birth came after your birthday, you need to count forward from the New Moon in the previous month. If you were born in a Leap Year, remember to count the 29th February. You can tell if your birth year was a Leap Year if the last two digits can be divided by four. Whatever the result, jot this number down so that you do not forget it.

STAGE 2 Take a look at Moon Table 2 on page 27. Down the left hand column look for the date of your birth. Now trace across to the month of your birth. Where the two meet you will find a letter. Copy this letter down alongside your Moon Age Day.

STAGE 3 Moon Table 3 on page 27 will supply you with the zodiac sign the Moon occupied on the day of your birth. Look for your Moon Age Day down the left hand column and then for the letter you found in Stage 2. Where the two converge you will find a zodiac sign and this is the sign occupied by the Moon on the day that you were born.

Your Zodiac Moon Sign Explained

You will find a profile of all zodiac Moon Signs on pages 28 to 31, showing in yet another way how astrology helps to make you into the individual that you are. In each daily entry of the Astral Diary you can find the zodiac position of the Moon for every day of the year. This also allows you to discover your lunar birthdays. Since the Moon passes through all the signs of the zodiac in about a month, you can expect something like twelve lunar birthdays each year. At these times you are likely to be emotionally steady and able to make the sort of decisions that have real, lasting value.

Moon Table I

YEAR	JUL	AUG	SEP	YEAR	JUL	AUG	SEP	YEAR	JUL	AUG	SEP
1919	27	25	23	1952	23	20	19	1985	17	16	14
1920	15	14	12	1953	11	9	8	1986	7	5	4
1921	5	3	2	1954	29	28	27	1987	25	24	23
1922	24	22	21	1955	19	17	16	1988	13	12	11
1923	14	12	10	1956	8	6	4	1989	3	1/31	29
1924	2/31	30	28	1957	27	25	23	1990	22	20	19
1925	20	19	18	1958	16	15	13	1991	11	9	8
1926	9	8	7	1959	6	4	3	1992	29	28	26
1927	28	27	25	1960	24	22	21	1993	19	17	16
1928	17	16	14	1961	12	11	10	1994	8	7	5
1929	6	5	3	1962	1/31	30	28	1995	27	26	24
1930	25	24	22	1963	20	19	17	1996	15	14	13
1931	15	13	12	1964	9	7	6	1997	4	3	2
1932	3	2/31	30	1965	28	26	25	1998	23	22	20
1933	22	21	19	1966	17	16	14	1999	13	11	10
1934	11	10	9	1967	7	5	4	2000	1/31	29	27
1935	30	29	27	1968	25	24	23	2001	20	19	17
1936	18	17	15	1969	13	12	11	2002	9	8	6
1937	8	6	4	1970	4	2	1	2003	28	27	26
1938	27	25	23	1971	22	20	19	2004	16	14	13
1939	16	15	13	1972	11	9	8	2005	6	4	3
1940	5	4	2	1973	29	28	27	2006	25	23	22
1941	24	22	21	1974	19	17	16	2007	15	13	12
1942	13	12	10	1975	9	7	5	2008	31	31	30
1943	2	1/30	29	1976	27	25	23	2009	22	20	19
1944	20	18	17	1977	16	14	13	2010	12	10	8
1945	9	8	6	1978	5	4	2	2011	2/31	29	27
1946	28	26	25	1979	24	22	21	2012	19	17	16
1947	17	16	14	1980	12	11	10	2013	7	6	4
1948	6	5	3	1981	1/31	29	28	2014	25	24	23
1949	25	24	23	1982	20	19	17	2015	16	15	13
1950	15	13	12	1983	10	8	7	2016	4	2	1
1951	4	2	1	1984	28	26	25	2017	23	22	20

Table 2

DAY	AUG	SEP
1	U	X
2	U	X
3	V	X
4	V	Y
5	V	Y
6	V	Y
7	V	Y
8	V	Y
9	V	Y
10	V	Y
11	V	Y
12	V	Y
13	V	Y
14	W	Z
15	W	Z
16	W	Z
17	W	Z
18	W	Z
19	W	Z
20	W	Z
21	W	Z
22	W	Z
23	W	Z
24	X	a
25	X	a
26	X	a
27	X	a
28	X	a
29	X	a
30	X	a
31	X	–

Table 3

M/D	U	V	W	X	Y	Z	a
0	LE	LE	LE	VI	VI	LI	LI
1	LE	VI	VI	VI	LI	LI	LI
2	VI	VI	VI	LI	LI	LI	LI
3	VI	VI	LI	LI	LI	SC	SC
4	LI	LI	LI	LI	SC	SC	SC
5	LI	LI	SC	SC	SC	SC	SA
6	LI	SC	SC	SC	SA	SA	SA
7	SC	SC	SA	SA	SA	SA	SA
8	SC	SC	SA	SA	SA	CP	CP
9	SA	SA	SA	SA	CP	CP	CP
10	SA	SA	CP	CP	CP	CP	AQ
11	CP	CP	CP	CP	AQ	AQ	AQ
12	CP	CP	AQ	AQ	AQ	AQ	PI
13	CP	CP	AQ	AQ	AQ	PI	PI
14	AQ	AQ	PI	PI	PI	PI	AR
15	AQ	AQ	PI	PI	PI	PI	AR
16	AQ	PI	PI	PI	AR	AR	AR
17	PI	PI	PI	AR	AR	AR	AR
18	PI	PI	AR	AR	AR	AR	TA
19	PI	AR	AR	AR	TA	TA	TA
20	AR	AR	TA	TA	TA	TA	GE
21	AR	TA	TA	TA	GE	GE	GE
22	TA	TA	TA	GE	GE	GE	GE
23	TA	TA	GE	GE	GE	GE	CA
24	TA	GE	GE	GE	CA	CA	CA
25	GE	GE	CA	CA	CA	CA	CA
26	GE	CA	CA	CA	LE	LE	LE
27	CA	CA	CA	LE	LE	LE	LE
28	CA	CA	LE	LE	LE	LE	VI
29	CA	LE	LE	LE	VI	VI	VI

AR = Aries, TA = Taurus, GE = Gemini, CA = Cancer, LE = Leo, VI = Virgo, LI = Libra, SC = Scorpio, SA = Sagittarius, CP = Capricorn, AQ = Aquarius, PI = Pisces

MOON SIGNS

Moon in Aries

You have a strong imagination, courage, determination and a desire to do things in your own way and forge your own path through life.

Originality is a key attribute; you are seldom stuck for ideas although your mind is changeable and you could take the time to focus on individual tasks. Often quick-tempered, you take orders from few people and live life at a fast pace. Avoid health problems by taking regular time out for rest and relaxation.

Emotionally, it is important that you talk to those you are closest to and work out your true feelings. Once you discover that people are there to help, there is less necessity for you to do everything yourself.

Moon in Taurus

The Moon in Taurus gives you a courteous and friendly manner, which means you are likely to have many friends.

The good things in life mean a lot to you, as Taurus is an Earth sign that delights in experiences which please the senses. Hence you are probably a lover of good food and drink, which may in turn mean you need to keep an eye on the bathroom scales, especially as looking good is also important to you.

Emotionally you are fairly stable and you stick by your own standards. Taureans do not respond well to change. Intuition also plays an important part in your life.

Moon in Gemini

You have a warm-hearted character, sympathetic and eager to help others. At times reserved, you can also be articulate and chatty: this is part of the paradox of Gemini, which always brings duplicity to the nature. You are interested in current affairs, have a good intellect, and are good company and likely to have many friends. Most of your friends have a high opinion of you and would be ready to defend you should the need arise. However, this is usually unnecessary, as you are quite capable of defending yourself in any verbal confrontation.

Travel is important to your inquisitive mind and you find intellectual stimulus in mixing with people from different cultures. You also gain much from reading, writing and the arts but you do need plenty of rest and relaxation in order to avoid fatigue.

Moon in Cancer

The Moon in Cancer at the time of birth is a fortunate position as Cancer is the Moon's natural home. This means that the qualities of compassion and understanding given by the Moon are especially enhanced in your nature, and you are friendly and sociable and cope well with emotional pressures. You cherish home and family life, and happily do the domestic tasks. Your surroundings are important to you and you hate squalor and filth. You are likely to have a love of music and poetry.

Your basic character, although at times changeable like the Moon itself, depends on symmetry. You aim to make your surroundings comfortable and harmonious, for yourself and those close to you.

Moon in Leo

The best qualities of the Moon and Leo come together to make you warmhearted, fair, ambitious and self-confident. With good organisational abilities, you invariably rise to a position of responsibility in your chosen career. This is fortunate as you don't enjoy being an 'also-ran' and would rather be an important part of a small organisation than a menial in a large one.

You should be lucky in love, and happy, provided you put in the effort to make a comfortable home for yourself and those close to you. It is likely that you will have a love of pleasure, sport, music and literature. Life brings you many rewards, most of them as a direct result of your own efforts, although you may be luckier than average and ready to make the best of any situation.

Moon in Virgo

You are endowed with good mental abilities and a keen receptive memory, but you are never ostentatious or pretentious. Naturally quite reserved, you still have many friends, especially of the opposite sex. Marital relationships must be discussed carefully and worked at so that they remain harmonious, as personal attachments can be a problem if you do not give them your full attention.

Talented and persevering, you possess artistic qualities and are a good homemaker. Earning your honours through genuine merit, you work long and hard towards your objectives but show little pride in your achievements. Many short journeys will be undertaken in your life.

Moon in Libra

With the Moon in Libra you are naturally popular and make friends easily. People like you, probably more than you realise, you bring fun to a party and are a natural diplomat. For all its good points, Libra is not the most stable of astrological signs and, as a result, your emotions can be a little unstable too. Therefore, although the Moon in Libra is said to be good for love and marriage, your Sun sign and Rising sign will have an important effect on your emotional and loving qualities.

You must remember to relate to others in your decision-making. Co-operation is crucial because Libra represents the 'balance' of life that can only be achieved through harmonious relationships. Conformity is not easy for you because Libra, an Air sign, likes its independence.

Moon in Scorpio

Some people might call you pushy. In fact, all you really want to do is to live life to the full and protect yourself and your family from the pressures of life. Take care to avoid giving the impression of being sarcastic or impulsive and use your energies wisely and constructively.

You have great courage and you invariably achieve your goals by force of personality and sheer effort. You are fond of mystery and are good at predicting the outcome of situations and events. Travel experiences can be beneficial to you.

You may experience problems if you do not take time to examine your motives in a relationship, and also if you allow jealousy, always a feature of Scorpio, to cloud your judgement.

Moon in Sagittarius

The Moon in Sagittarius helps to make you a generous individual with humanitarian qualities and a kind heart. Restlessness may be intrinsic as your mind is seldom still. Perhaps because of this, you have a need for change that could lead you to several major moves during your adult life. You are not afraid to stand your ground when you know your judgement is right, you speak directly and have good intuition.

At work you are quick, efficient and versatile and so you make an ideal employee. You need work to be intellectually demanding and do not enjoy tedious routines.

In relationships, you anger quickly if faced with stupidity or deception, though you are just as quick to forgive and forget. Emotionally, there are times when your heart rules your head.

Moon in Capricorn

The Moon in Capricorn makes you popular and likely to come into the public eye in some way. The watery Moon is not entirely comfortable in the Earth sign of Capricorn and this may lead to some difficulties in the early years of life. An initial lack of creative ability and indecision must be overcome before the true qualities of patience and perseverance inherent in Capricorn can show through.

You have good administrative ability and are a capable worker, and if you are careful you can accumulate wealth. But you must be cautious and take professional advice in partnerships, as you are open to deception. You may be interested in social or welfare work, which suit your organisational skills and sympathy for others.

Moon in Aquarius

The Moon in Aquarius makes you an active and agreeable person with a friendly, easy-going nature. Sympathetic to the needs of others, you flourish in a laid-back atmosphere. You are broad-minded, fair and open to suggestion, although sometimes you have an unconventional quality which others can find hard to understand.

You are interested in the strange and curious, and in old articles and places. You enjoy trips to these places and gain much from them. Political, scientific and educational work interests you and you might choose a career in science or technology.

Money-wise, you make gains through innovation and concentration and Lunar Aquarians often tackle more than one job at a time. In love you are kind and honest.

Moon in Pisces

You have a kind, sympathetic nature, somewhat retiring at times, but you always take account of others' feelings and help when you can.

Personal relationships may be problematic, but as life goes on you can learn from your experiences and develop a better understanding of yourself and the world around you.

You have a fondness for travel, appreciate beauty and harmony and hate disorder and strife. You may be fond of literature and would make a good writer or speaker yourself. You have a creative imagination and may come across as an incurable romantic. You have strong intuition, maybe bordering on a mediumistic quality, which sets you apart from the mass. You may not be rich in cash terms, but your personal gifts are worth more than gold.

VIRGO IN LOVE

D iscover how compatible you are with people from the same and other signs of the zodiac. Five stars equals a match made in heaven!

Virgo meets Virgo

Unlike many same-sign combinations this is not a five-star pairing, for one very good reason. Virgo needs to react with other signs to reveal its hidden best side. Two Virgoans together, although enjoying some happiness, will not present a dynamic, sparkling and carefree appearance. They should run an efficient and financially sound household, but that all-important ingredient, passion, may be distinctly low-key. Star rating: ***

Virgo meets Libra

There have been some rare occasions when this match has found great success, but usually the inward-looking Virgoan depresses the naturally gregarious Libran. Libra appears self-confident but is not so beneath the surface and needs encouragement to develop inner confidence, which may not come from Virgo. Constancy can be a problem for Libra, who also tires easily and may find Virgo dull. A less serious approach from Virgo is needed to make this work. Star rating: **

Virgo meets Scorpio

There are one or two potential difficulties here, but there is also a meeting point from which to overcome them. Virgo is very caring and protective, a trait which Scorpio understands and even emulates. Both signs are consistent, but also sarcastic. Scorpio will impress Virgo with its serious side, and may also uncover a hidden passion in Virgo which all too often lies deep within its Earth-sign nature. Material success is very likely, with Virgo taking the lion's share of domestic chores and family responsibilities. Star rating: ***

Virgo meets Sagittarius

There can be some strange happenings in this relationship. Sagittarius and Virgo view life so differently there are always new discoveries. Virgo is much more of a home bird than Sagittarius, but that won't matter if the Archer introduces its hectic social life gradually. More importantly, Sagittarius understands that it takes Virgo a long time to free its hidden 'inner sprite', but once free it will be fun all the way – until Virgo's thrifty nature takes over. There are great possibilities, but effort is required. Star rating: ***

Virgo meets Capricorn

One of the best possible combinations, because Virgo and Capricorn have an instinctive understanding. Both signs know the value of dedicated hard work and apply it equally in a relationship and other areas of life. Two of the most practical signs, nothing is beyond their ken, even if to outsiders they appear rather sterile or lacking in 'oomph'. What matters most is that the individuals are happy, and with so much in common, the likelihood of mutual material success and a shared devotion to home and family, there isn't much doubt of that. Star rating: *****

Virgo meets Aquarius

Aquarius is a strange sign because no matter how well one knows it, it always manages to surprise, and for this reason, against the odds, it's quite likely that Aquarius will form a successful relationship with Virgo. Aquarius is changeable, unpredictable and often quite 'odd' while Virgo is steady, a fuss-pot and very practical. Herein lies the key. What one sign needs, the other provides and that may be the surest recipe for success imaginable. On-lookers may not know why the couple are happy, but they will recognise that this is the case. Star rating: ****

Virgo meets Pisces

This looks an unpromising match from beginning to end. There are exceptions to every rule, particularly where Pisces is concerned, but these two signs are both so deep it's hard to imagine that they could ever find what makes the other tick. Virgo's ruminations are extremely materialistic, while Pisces exists in a world of deep-felt, poorly expressed emotion. Pisces and Virgo might find they don't talk much, so only in a contemplative, almost monastic, match would they ever get on. Still, in a vast zodiac, anything is possible. Star rating: **

Virgo meets Aries

Neither of these signs really understands the other, and that could easily lead to a clash. Virgo is so pedantic, which will drive Aries up the wall, while Aries always wants to be moving on to the next objective before Virgo is even settled with the last one. It will take time for these two to get to know each other, but this is a great business matching. If a personal relationship is seen in these terms then the prognosis can be quite good, but on the whole, this is not an inspiring match. Star rating: ***

Virgo meets Taurus

This is a difficult basis for a successful relationship, and yet it often works. Both signs are from the Earth element, so have a common-sense approach to life. They have a mutual understanding, and share many interests. Taurus understands and copes well with Virgo's fussy nature, while Virgo revels in the Bull's tidy and artistic qualities. Both sides are committed to achieving lasting material success. There won't be fireworks, and the match may lack a certain 'spiritual' feel, but as that works both ways it may not be a problem. Star rating: *****

Virgo meets Gemini

The fact that both these signs are ruled by the planet Mercury might at first seem good but, unfortunately, Mercury works very differently in these signs. Gemini is untidy, flighty, quick, changeable and easily bored, while Virgo is fastidious, steady and constant. If Virgo is willing to accept some anarchy all can be well, but this not usually the case. Virgoans are deep thinkers and may find Gemini a little superficial. This pair can be compatible intellectually, though even this side isn't without its problems. Star rating: ***

Virgo meets Cancer

This match has little chance of success, for fairly simple reasons: Cancer's generous affection will be submerged by the Virgoan depths, not because Virgo is uncaring but because it expresses itself so differently. As both signs are naturally quiet, things might become a bit boring. They would be mutually supportive, possibly financially successful and have a very tidy house, but they won't share much sparkle, enthusiasm, risk-taking or passion. If this pair were stranded on a desert island, they might live at different ends of it. Star rating: **

Virgo meets Leo

There is a chance for this couple, but it won't be trouble-free. Leo and Virgo view life very differently: Virgo is of a serious nature and struggles to relate to Leo's relentless optimism and cheerfulness and can find it annoying. Leo, meanwhile, may find Virgo stodgy, sometimes dark and uninspiring. The saving grace comes through communication – Leo knows how to make Virgo talk, which is what it needs. If this pair find happiness, though, it may be a case of opposites attract! Star rating: ***

VENUS:
THE PLANET OF LOVE

If you look up at the sky around sunset or sunrise you will often see Venus in close attendance to the Sun. It is arguably one of the most beautiful sights of all and there is little wonder that historically it became associated with the goddess of love. But although Venus does play an important part in the way you view love and in the way others see you romantically, this is only one of the spheres of influence that it enjoys in your overall character.

Venus has a part to play in the more cultured side of your life and has much to do with your appreciation of art, literature, music and general creativity. Even the way you look is responsive to the part of the zodiac that Venus occupied at the start of your life, though this fact is also down to your Sun sign and Ascending sign. If, at the time you were born, Venus occupied one of the more gregarious zodiac signs, you will be more likely to wear your heart on your sleeve, as well as to be more attracted to entertainment, social gatherings and good company. If on the other hand Venus occupied a quiet zodiac sign at the time of your birth, you would tend to be more retiring and less willing to shine in public situations.

It's good to know what part the planet Venus plays in your life, for it can have a great bearing on the way you appear to the rest of the world and since we all have to mix with others, you can learn to make the very best of what Venus has to offer you.

One of the great complications in the past has always been trying to establish exactly what zodiac position Venus enjoyed when you were born, because the planet is notoriously difficult to track. However, I have solved that problem by creating a table that is exclusive to your Sun sign, which you will find on the following page.

Establishing your Venus sign could not be easier. Just look up the year of your birth on the page opposite and you will see a sign of the Zodiac. This was the sign that Venus occupied in the period covered by your sign in that year. If Venus occupied more than one sign during the period, this is indicated by the date on which the sign changed, and the name of the new sign. For instance, if you were born in 1950, Venus was in Leo until the 10th September, after which time it was in Virgo. If you were born before 10th September your Venus sign is Leo, if you were born on or after 10th September, your Venus sign is Virgo. Once you have established the position of Venus at the time of your birth, you can then look in the pages which follow to see how this has a bearing on your life as a whole.

1919 VIRGO
1920 VIRGO / 5.9 LIBRA
1921 CANCER / 31.8 LEO
1922 LIBRA / 8.9 SCORPIO
1923 LEO / 28.8 VIRGO /
  20.9 LIBRA
1924 CANCER / 9.9 LEO
1925 LIBRA / 16.9 SCORPIO
1926 LEO / 12.9 VIRGO
1927 VIRGO
1928 VIRGO / 5.9 LIBRA
1929 CANCER / 31.8 LEO
1930 LIBRA / 7.9 SCORPIO
1931 LEO / 28.8 VIRGO /
  20.9 LIBRA
1932 CANCER / 9.9 LEO
1933 LIBRA / 16.9 SCORPIO
1934 LEO / 11.9 VIRGO
1935 VIRGO
1936 VIRGO / 4.9 LIBRA
1937 CANCER / 31.8 LEO
1938 LIBRA / 7.9 SCORPIO
1939 LEO / 27.8 VIRGO /
  19.9 LIBRA
1940 CANCER / 9.9 LEO
1941 LIBRA / 15.9 SCORPIO
1942 LEO / 11.9 VIRGO
1943 VIRGO
1944 VIRGO / 4.9 LIBRA
1945 CANCER / 30.8 LEO
1946 LIBRA / 7.9 SCORPIO
1947 LEO / 27.8 VIRGO /
  18.9 LIBRA
1948 CANCER / 9.9 LEO
1949 LIBRA / 15.9 SCORPIO
1950 LEO / 10.9 VIRGO
1951 VIRGO
1952 VIRGO / 3.9 LIBRA
1953 CANCER / 30.8 LEO
1954 LIBRA / 7.9 SCORPIO
1955 LEO / 26.8 VIRGO /
  17.9 LIBRA
1956 CANCER / 8.9 LEO
1957 LIBRA / 15.9 SCORPIO
1958 LEO / 10.9 VIRGO
1959 VIRGO / 20.9 LEO
1960 VIRGO / 3.9 LIBRA
1961 CANCER / 30.8 LEO
1962 LIBRA / 8.9 SCORPIO
1963 LEO / 26.8 VIRGO /
  17.9 LIBRA
1964 CANCER / 8.9 LEO
1965 LIBRA / 15.9 SCORPIO
1966 LEO / 9.9 VIRGO

1967 VIRGO / 10.9 LEO
1968 VIRGO / 2.9 LIBRA
1969 CANCER / 29.8 LEO
1970 LIBRA / 8.9 SCORPIO
1971 LEO / 25.8 VIRGO /
  16.9 LIBRA
1972 CANCER / 8.9 LEO
1973 LIBRA / 14.9 SCORPIO
1974 LEO / 8.9 VIRGO
1975 VIRGO / 3.9 LEO
1976 VIRGO / 2.9 LIBRA
1977 CANCER / 29.8 LEO
1978 LIBRA / 8.9 SCORPIO
1979 VIRGO / 16.9 LIBRA
1980 CANCER / 8.9 LEO
1981 LIBRA / 14.9 SCORPIO
1982 LEO / 7.9 VIRGO
1983 VIRGO / 28.8 LEO
1984 VIRGO / 2.9 LIBRA
1985 CANCER / 28.8 LEO
1986 LIBRA / 8.9 SCORPIO
1987 VIRGO / 15.9 LIBRA
1988 CANCER / 7.9 LEO
1989 LIBRA / 13.9 SCORPIO
1990 LEO / 7.9 VIRGO
1991 LEO
1992 VIRGO / 1.9 LIBRA
1993 CANCER / 28.8 LEO
1994 LIBRA / 8.9 SCORPIO
1995 VIRGO / 15.9 LIBRA
1996 CANCER / 7.9 LEO
1997 LIBRA / 12.9 SCORPIO
1998 LEO / 6.9 VIRGO
1999 LEO
2000 VIRGO / 1.9 LIBRA
2001 CANCER / 28.8 LEO
2002 LIBRA / 8.9 SCORPIO
2003 VIRGO / 15.9 LIBRA
2004 CANCER / 6.9 LEO
2005 LIBRA / 10.9 SCORPIO
2006 LEO / 4.9 VIRGO
2007 LEO
2008 VIRGO / 1.9 LIBRA
2009 CANCER / 28.8 LEO
2010 LIBRA / 8.9 SCORPIO
2011 VIRGO / 15.9 LIBRA
2012 CANCER / 6.9 LEO
2013 LIBRA / 10.9 SCORPIO
2014 LEO / 4.9 VIRGO
2015 LEO
2016 VIRGO / 31.8 LIBRA
2017 CANCER / 28.8 LEO

VENUS THROUGH THE ZODIAC SIGNS

Venus in Aries

Amongst other things, the position of Venus in Aries indicates a fondness for travel, music and all creative pursuits. Your nature tends to be affectionate and you would try not to create confusion or difficulty for others if it could be avoided. Many people with this planetary position have a great love of the theatre, and mental stimulation is of the greatest importance. Early romantic attachments are common with Venus in Aries, so it is very important to establish a genuine sense of romantic continuity. Early marriage is not recommended, especially if it is based on sympathy. You may give your heart a little too readily on occasions.

Venus in Taurus

You are capable of very deep feelings and your emotions tend to last for a very long time. This makes you a trusting partner and lover, whose constancy is second to none. In life you are precise and careful and always try to do things the right way. Although this means an ordered life, which you are comfortable with, it can also lead you to be rather too fussy for your own good. Despite your pleasant nature, you are very fixed in your opinions and quite able to speak your mind. Others are attracted to you and historical astrologers always quoted this position of Venus as being very fortunate in terms of marriage. However, if you find yourself involved in a failed relationship, it could take you a long time to trust again.

Venus in Gemini

As with all associations related to Gemini, you tend to be quite versatile, anxious for change and intelligent in your dealings with the world at large. You may gain money from more than one source but you are equally good at spending it. There is an inference here that you are a good communicator, via either the written or the spoken word, and you love to be in the company of interesting people. Always on the look-out for culture, you may also be very fond of music, and love to indulge the curious and cultured side of your nature. In romance you tend to have more than one relationship and could find yourself associated with someone who has previously been a friend or even a distant relative.

Venus in Cancer

You often stay close to home because you are very fond of family and enjoy many of your most treasured moments when you are with those you love. Being naturally sympathetic, you will always do anything you can to support those around you, even people you hardly know at all. This charitable side of your nature is your most noticeable trait and is one of the reasons why others are naturally so fond of you. Being receptive and in some cases even psychic, you can see through to the soul of most of those with whom you come into contact. You may not commence too many romantic attachments but when you do give your heart, it tends to be unconditionally.

Venus in Leo

It must become quickly obvious to almost anyone you meet that you are kind, sympathetic and yet determined enough to stand up for anyone or anything that is truly important to you. Bright and sunny, you warm the world with your natural enthusiasm and would rarely do anything to hurt those around you, or at least not intentionally. In romance you are ardent and sincere, though some may find your style just a little overpowering. Gains come through your contacts with other people and this could be especially true with regard to romance, for love and money often come hand in hand for those who were born with Venus in Leo. People claim to understand you, though you are more complex than you seem.

Venus in Virgo

Your nature could well be fairly quiet no matter what your Sun sign might be, though this fact often manifests itself as an inner peace and would not prevent you from being basically sociable. Some delays and even the odd disappointment in love cannot be ruled out with this planetary position, though it's a fact that you will usually find the happiness you look for in the end. Catapulting yourself into romantic entanglements that you know to be rather ill-advised is not sensible, and it would be better to wait before you committed yourself exclusively to any one person. It is the essence of your nature to serve the world at large and through doing so it is possible that you will attract money at some stage in your life.

Venus in Libra

Venus is very comfortable in Libra and bestows upon those people who have this planetary position a particular sort of kindness that is easy to recognise. This is a very good position for all sorts of friendships and also for romantic attachments that usually bring much joy into your life. Few individuals with Venus in Libra would avoid marriage and since you are capable of great depths of love, it is likely that you will find a contented personal life. You like to mix with people of integrity and intelligence but don't take kindly to scruffy surroundings or work that means getting your hands too dirty. Careful speculation, good business dealings and money through marriage all seem fairly likely.

Venus in Scorpio

You are quite open and tend to spend money quite freely, even on those occasions when you don't have very much. Although your intentions are always good, there are times when you get yourself in to the odd scrape and this can be particularly true when it comes to romance, which you may come to late or from a rather unexpected direction. Certainly you have the power to be happy and to make others contented on the way, but you find the odd stumbling block on your journey through life and it could seem that you have to work harder than those around you. As a result of this, you gain a much deeper understanding of the true value of personal happiness than many people ever do, and are likely to achieve true contentment in the end.

Venus in Sagittarius

You are lighthearted, cheerful and always able to see the funny side of any situation. These facts enhance your popularity, which is especially high with members of the opposite sex. You should never have to look too far to find romantic interest in your life, though it is just possible that you might be too willing to commit yourself before you are certain that the person in question is right for you. Part of the problem here extends to other areas of life too. The fact is that you like variety in everything and so can tire of situations that fail to offer it. All the same, if you choose wisely and learn to understand your restless side, then great happiness can be yours.

Venus in Capricorn

The most notable trait that comes from Venus in this position is that it makes you trustworthy and able to take on all sorts of responsibilities in life. People are instinctively fond of you and love you all the more because you are always ready to help those who are in any form of need. Social and business popularity can be yours and there is a magnetic quality to your nature that is particularly attractive in a romantic sense. Anyone who wants a partner for a lover, a spouse and a good friend too would almost certainly look in your direction. Constancy is the hallmark of your nature and unfaithfulness would go right against the grain. You might sometimes be a little too trusting.

Venus in Aquarius

This location of Venus offers a fondness for travel and a desire to try out something new at every possible opportunity. You are extremely easy to get along with and tend to have many friends from varied backgrounds, classes and inclinations. You like to live a distinct sort of life and gain a great deal from moving about, both in a career sense and with regard to your home. It is not out of the question that you could form a romantic attachment to someone who comes from far away or be attracted to a person of a distinctly artistic and original nature. What you cannot stand is jealousy, for you have friends of both sexes and would want to keep things that way.

Venus in Pisces

The first thing people tend to notice about you is your wonderful, warm smile. Being very charitable by nature you will do anything to help others, even if you don't know them well. Much of your life may be spent sorting out situations for other people, but it is very important to feel that you are living for yourself too. In the main, you remain cheerful, and tend to be quite attractive to members of the opposite sex. Where romantic attachments are concerned, you could be drawn to people who are significantly older or younger than yourself or to someone with a unique career or point of view. It might be best for you to avoid marrying whilst you are still very young.

HOW THE DIAGRAMS WORK

Through the picture diagrams in the Astral Diary I want to help you to plot your year. With them you can see where the positive and negative aspects will be found in each month. To make the most of them, all you have to do is remember where and when!

Let me show you how they work ...

THE MONTH AT A GLANCE

Just as there are twelve separate zodiac signs, so astrologers believe that each sign has twelve separate aspects to life. Each of the twelve segments relates to a different personal aspect. I list them all every month so that their meanings are always clear.

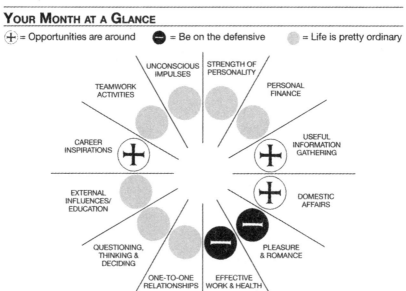

I have designed this chart to show you how and when these twelve different aspects are being influenced throughout the year. When there is a shaded circle, nothing out of the ordinary is to be expected. However, when a circle turns white with a plus sign, the influence is positive. Where the circle is black with a minus sign, it is a negative.

YOUR ENERGY RHYTHM CHART

Below is a picture diagram in which I link your zodiac group to the rhythm of the Moon. In doing this I have calculated when you will be gaining strength from its influence and equally when you may be weakened by it.

If you think of yourself as being like the tides of the ocean then you may understand how your own energies must also rise and fall. And if you understand how it works and when it is working, then you can better organise your activities to achieve more and get things done more easily.

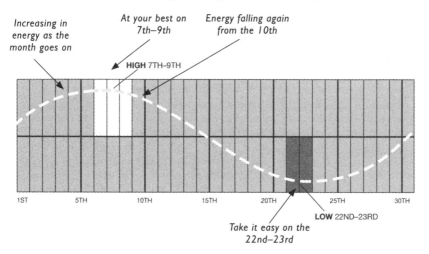

THE KEY DAYS

Some of the entries are in **bold**, which indicates the working of astrological cycles in your life. Look out for them each week as they are the best days to take action or make decisions. The daily text tells you which area of your life to focus on.

MERCURY RETROGRADE

The Mercury symbol (☿) indicates that Mercury is retrograde on that day. Since Mercury governs communication, the fact that it appears to be moving backwards when viewed from the Earth at this time should warn you that your communication skills are not likely to be at their best and you could expect some setbacks.

VIRGO: YOUR YEAR IN BRIEF

Trends during January and February may not offer you everything you want from life but they do have the advantage of making you extremely efficient and willing to go as far as is necessary in order to get what you want. It's important to give and take regarding family matters and also at work, but stick to your own opinions in the end. In many respects you could hardly start a year in a better frame of mind and that shows clearly as the weeks advance.

As the spring arrives, the month of March brings a lightening of your spirit as the Sun gets higher in the sky. You will be quite keen to get ahead and anxious to show how much you have learnt. April will see you making significant progress in matters of love and in relationships generally, all of which contributes to a more exciting and noteworthy period. Don't gamble too much at this time and when it comes to decisions, play your cards close to your chest.

The early summer may turn out to be one of the best times for you. You should be feeling less constrained and will have every chance to spread your wings, especially in terms of travel. There are some small but significant financial gains to be made during May and June, and many Virgoans could be thinking about changes to their careers now.

July and August could turn out to be the busiest months of the year for you, again in terms of travel and general movement in your life as a whole. You appear to be trying out new things and will also be quite competitive and sporting throughout the period. Rules and regulations might be irritating, and it is quite clear that you can be both radical and even unique in your approach. You may surprise people at this time.

As the autumn arrives, September and October should see you achieving more of your objectives and also on the ball when it comes to love and romance. New relationships may commence now and there is a strong sense of purpose in almost everything you do. If colleagues are behaving strangely, accept their point of view, no matter how odd it might seem, though in the end go with what suits you.

The final two months of the year, November and December, will find you as busy as ever and probably more successful than at any stage previously. Things seem to come to you, even some things you had abandoned forever. By Christmas you should have everything more or less the way you want it to be, though it is quite possible that right at the end of the year you will seem to run out of steam and will need to take the year end fairly steadily.

January

2017

YOUR MONTH AT A GLANCE

(+) = Opportunities are around   ⊖ = Be on the defensive   ⬤ = Life is pretty ordinary

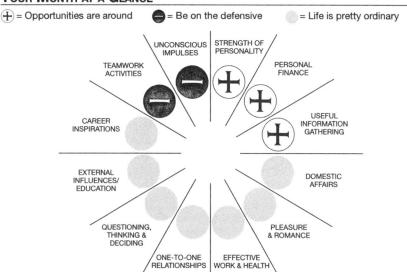

JANUARY HIGHS AND LOWS

Here I show you how the rhythms of the Moon will affect you this month. Like the tide, your energies and abilities will rise and fall with its pattern. When it is above the centre line, go for it, when it is below, you should be resting.

HIGH 16TH–17TH

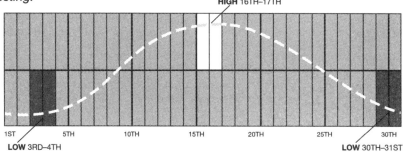

1ST   5TH   10TH   15TH   20TH   25TH   30TH

LOW 3RD–4TH   LOW 30TH–31ST

45

1 SUNDAY ☿ *Moon Age Day 4   Moon Sign Aquarius*

Domestic relationships should be a positive breeze at present and you will be especially drawn towards your home and family members at the start of the new year. Active and enterprising when away from your own castle, you have good ideas about the way things should be. Take care how you put these across, though, and don't inadvertently annoy someone.

2 MONDAY ☿ *Moon Age Day 5   Moon Sign Aquarius*

In social settings you can positively shine at the moment and you won't be backward when it comes to expressing your opinions. There is someone around you just now who really inspires you and there are other people who are able to help your week go with a swing after a steady start. New personalities seem to be cropping up in your life all the time.

3 TUESDAY ☿ *Moon Age Day 6   Moon Sign Pisces*

The Moon moves into your opposite zodiac sign today. This is the part of the month known as the lunar low and it will often make you quieter, slightly less optimistic and more inclined to seek your own company. Nothing is likely to be going very wrong – it's simply that you keep yourself to yourself.

4 WEDNESDAY ☿ *Moon Age Day 7   Moon Sign Pisces*

You continue to inhabit your own shell most of the time and won't be drawn out into situations that seem either threatening or too energetic. This might surprise your friends and colleagues but if they have known you for any length of time they will be quite aware of the way your mind works. Don't worry because things will soon change.

5 THURSDAY ☿ *Moon Age Day 8   Moon Sign Aries*

You might not be making quite the level of progress at work today that you had hoped or expected and if this is the case you simply need to have a little patience. Don't worry about situations you can't alter, concentrate on those you can. Prepare for a little bad luck with mechanical or electrical devices.

6 FRIDAY ☿ *Moon Age Day 9   Moon Sign Aries*

Give yourself a pat on the back for something that turns out right early today but don't get complacent. There is plenty more to do and lots of situations you can address successfully. Maintain reasonable expectations of yourself and allow yourself to settle to tasks comfortably.

Your Daily Guide to January 2017

7 SATURDAY ☿ *Moon Age Day 10   Moon Sign Taurus*

You could be in two minds regarding a practical decision but this is most unlike you and so may lead to a little frustration. If you really can't decide what to do the best way forward for the immediate future might be to do nothing at all. Put a few things on the backburner and concentrate on things you find easier.

8 SUNDAY *Moon Age Day 11   Moon Sign Taurus*

There is just a possibility that you could become involved in disputes today and that wouldn't make for a very useful or peaceful sort of Sunday. Keep some of your more radical opinions to yourself and opt to do something that keeps you full occupied. Some Virgos might be keen on a shopping spree.

9 MONDAY *Moon Age Day 12   Moon Sign Gemini*

Business encounters are important today but could also put you under a degree of pressure if you don't think before you speak. You could come across people who are in an excellent position to help you and it would not be sensible to annoy them – even inadvertently. In your love life you are far more tactful.

10 TUESDAY *Moon Age Day 13   Moon Sign Gemini*

Everyday issues should go according to plan and although you may not get everything you want today, when it matters the most you should be succeeding. Excitement may have to wait for a few days but what really matters the most to Virgo now is the solidity of life, so you won't be champing at the bit.

11 WEDNESDAY *Moon Age Day 14   Moon Sign Cancer*

You have a spring in your step as the month of January progresses. You seem to be especially optimistic just at the moment and won't be fazed by issues that could really have troubled you only a month or two ago. Most of your decisions are instinctive today, which is not altogether unusual for you.

12 THURSDAY *Moon Age Day 15   Moon Sign Cancer*

Now you can reap all the benefits of the domestic scene and without having to put in much effort yourself. The fact is that your desire to achieve outstrips your ability just now and at least when you are at home other people will help you out. Concentration may be lacking but personal warmth is all around you.

13 FRIDAY
Moon Age Day 16   Moon Sign Cancer

There are many small adjustments to be made today if you want to get things working just the way you need them to be. Virgo rarely stops tinkering, though your thought processes remain as solid as ever and the view you have of your own future is second-to-none in its accuracy. Finances look stronger than you may have expected.

14 SATURDAY
Moon Age Day 17   Moon Sign Leo

The need for your own personal input is strong at the moment but that only leads to more frustration if you don't seem to be getting on as well as you would wish. Nothing short of miracles will satisfy you under present planetary trends and perhaps you need to remind yourself that you are only human – which is true, even for Virgo.

15 SUNDAY
Moon Age Day 18   Moon Sign Leo

Maximise your potential today. As a Virgo, you always have an eye on the future and wish to provide for yourself in case of rainy days. Virgoans who have been off-colour of late should now find themselves feeling a great deal better and more energetic.

16 MONDAY
Moon Age Day 19   Moon Sign Virgo

Today the Moon returns to Virgo and brings that part of the month known as the lunar high. You become more inspirational, louder and keen to get involved in anything. Some people might shy away from your company but that's only because they find it hard to keep up with your lightning-quick thought processes.

17 TUESDAY
Moon Age Day 20   Moon Sign Virgo

You are still firing on all cylinders and shouldn't have any problem at all impressing the most important people. Socially speaking you will also be on top form and although you may have been quite happy to leave all the interactions and functions behind after the New Year it seems you are right back in gear now.

18 WEDNESDAY
Moon Age Day 21   Moon Sign Libra

There is plenty of affection coming in your direction and some of it could be arriving from previously unexpected directions. It is only now that you realise just how fond of you a particular person is. Your social life could be on a high and it is likely that you are about to become involved in groups or associations that are new to you.

19 THURSDAY
Moon Age Day 22   Moon Sign Libra

There are many potential distractions about today and all of them are so interesting you can't avoid being slightly diverted by them. All the same the general trends are good and you can still remain focused on those matters you consider to be of supreme importance. In a practical sense things will get done today, but not very quickly.

20 FRIDAY
Moon Age Day 23   Moon Sign Scorpio

Take the opportunity that comes along now to broaden your horizons in some way. There may well be an opportunity to travel or some new responsibility coming up at work. Be open and ready for whatever life puts your way. Your past actions have brought you to this particular place at this time.

21 SATURDAY
Moon Age Day 24   Moon Sign Scorpio

Get ready to make tracks and to start new projects whenever you get the chance. This is a weekend that could be especially good in a social sense and which brings more in the way of close contacts with others. There are some real personalities around at the moment and they will brighten your life.

22 SUNDAY
Moon Age Day 25   Moon Sign Scorpio

Focus your sights on your social life because you have everything it takes right now to mix business with pleasure. There are some uplifting and potentially life-changing experiences on the way but you will have to be alert in order to fully recognise them. Unfortunately, there might not be as much time today for loved ones as you would wish.

23 MONDAY
Moon Age Day 26   Moon Sign Sagittarius

On the whole you should find money matters easy to negotiate and it looks as though there might also be slightly more cash around than you expected. It is possible for you to bring a certain project to a satisfactory conclusion but there will be no time to stand still. The planets right now suggest that action and incentive is what fires you up.

24 TUESDAY
Moon Age Day 27   Moon Sign Sagittarius

This is a day when you can press ahead with great confidence. The Sun has moved on in your chart, now bringing a more considered and slightly quieter way of looking at situations, but you are none the less potent for that. Actually you may be even more striking when seen by others – some of them actively want to follow your lead.

25 WEDNESDAY *Moon Age Day 28   Moon Sign Capricorn*

Today is a time of renewal and a period when you can look at your life in a very positive way. The planets also suggest that the time is right to get rid of any baggage that is now longer of use to you. This may include some of the physical trappings that surround you at home but is just as likely to represent outmoded ideas and concepts.

26 THURSDAY *Moon Age Day 29   Moon Sign Capricorn*

Though right now you are energetic and strong willed, your ego could be too high for your own good. You may even show yourself as being volatile, which isn't too uncommon for Virgo types. Rein in your emotions somewhat and avoid allowing yourself to become irritated, even when people provoke you. Also learn to laugh at yourself.

27 FRIDAY *Moon Age Day 0   Moon Sign Capricorn*

Put your best foot forward today and avoid being slowed down by irrelevant details or by people who seem to have a very negative sort of attitude to life generally. You are now in a very positive frame of mind and will be inclined to focus on what is absolutely necessary and avoid involvement in pointless exercises.

28 SATURDAY *Moon Age Day 1   Moon Sign Aquarius*

Most people seem to be in your good books at the moment, partly because you have what it takes to make excuses for others and because you have a good understanding of what makes them tick. Younger family members especially tend to turn to you for help and advice. This you will be happy to offer, along with some practical help.

29 SUNDAY *Moon Age Day 2   Moon Sign Aquarius*

When it comes to getting on with people you will have no trouble whatsoever. Today provides a little oasis of energy and determination ahead of a slightly less favourable period. End the weekend on a high note and mix with those family members or close friends who you are always pleased to have around.

30 MONDAY *Moon Age Day 3   Moon Sign Pisces*

Now you are in for a couple of quieter days. The Moon has moved into your opposite zodiac sign, bringing the lunar low around again. It will be necessary to check and recheck all details and to move forward slowly and steadily. There's nothing strange about this for the often-cautious Virgo.

31 TUESDAY
Moon Age Day 4   Moon Sign Pisces

It might be difficult for you to get an objective picture of certain facts and figures in your life and rather than proceeding without the necessary information, you will probably choose to watch and wait instead. Family concerns are likely to be uppermost in your mind and you may not wander far from home today.

2017

YOUR MONTH AT A GLANCE

$\oplus$ = Opportunities are around $\ominus$ = Be on the defensive   ⬤ = Life is pretty ordinary

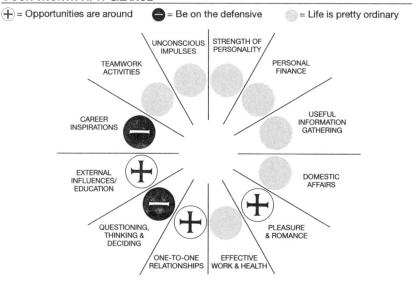

UNCONSCIOUS IMPULSES

STRENGTH OF PERSONALITY

TEAMWORK ACTIVITIES

PERSONAL FINANCE

CAREER INSPIRATIONS

USEFUL INFORMATION GATHERING

EXTERNAL INFLUENCES/ EDUCATION

DOMESTIC AFFAIRS

QUESTIONING, THINKING & DECIDING

PLEASURE & ROMANCE

ONE-TO-ONE RELATIONSHIPS

EFFECTIVE WORK & HEALTH

FEBRUARY HIGHS AND LOWS

Here I show you how the rhythms of the Moon will affect you this month. Like the tide, your energies and abilities will rise and fall with its pattern. When it is above the centre line, go for it, when it is below, you should be resting.

HIGH 12TH–13TH

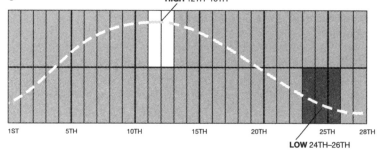

1ST   5TH   10TH   15TH   20TH   25TH   28TH

LOW 24TH–26TH

1 WEDNESDAY
Moon Age Day 5   Moon Sign Aries

This is a time when your domestic side is really on display and for much of the rest of this week you will find yourself completing one job or another at home. Family ties will be especially important to you, though it would also be sensible to concentrate on good friends, one or two of whom are on the verge of helping you out big time.

2 THURSDAY
Moon Age Day 6   Moon Sign Aries

Along comes a period that brings out high-spirited behaviour and an overwhelming desire to do something new. It won't satisfy you at the moment to simply jog along and if you could make almost any sort of trip right now the level of enjoyment that attends it should be high. Routines are for the birds under present trends.

3 FRIDAY
Moon Age Day 7   Moon Sign Aries

Nothing seems to slow you down at present and you have exactly what it takes to make a singular impression on people you see as important. Friends may rely on you heavily but you won't see this as any sort of imposition. On the contrary you will be doing all you can to help your pals sort out their own lives.

4 SATURDAY
Moon Age Day 8   Moon Sign Taurus

Someone you know well and maybe a competitor probably seems to be doing rather better than you are, a fact that could lead to a little envy or jealousy on your part. This should be strenuously avoided and instead you should show how pleased you are on their behalf. A little humility can go a long way and lifts your popularity.

5 SUNDAY
Moon Age Day 9   Moon Sign Taurus

If there are any heavy emotional pressures surrounding you at the moment you should do whatever is necessary to sort these out once and for all. This might lead to a heart-to-heart chat but it is just as important for you to listen as to have your say. Simply understanding another point of view could be all it takes.

6 MONDAY
Moon Age Day 10   Moon Sign Gemini

It will be almost impossible today to stick to what you know and yet still get ahead of the field. You need to learn new things and to familiarise yourself with subject matter that has not been part of your life up to now. It's amazing how quickly you can do this and how much you will surprise colleagues and friends with your new knowledge.

7 TUESDAY   *Moon Age Day 11   Moon Sign Gemini*

Your domestic life should be improving around now and it looks as though you will be thinking in terms of an early spring clean. This is not so much a case of chasing away the dust as of leaving behind items and situations that are no longer of any use to you. You need to travel light in the weeks and months ahead.

8 WEDNESDAY   *Moon Age Day 12   Moon Sign Cancer*

Events taking place around you now may be inspirational and could lead to new social contacts. Don't rule out the possibility of becoming involved in some sort of activity that hasn't appealed to you at all in the past. Virgo gradually becomes more competitive under present planetary trends.

9 THURSDAY   *Moon Age Day 13   Moon Sign Cancer*

Your charisma and charm are definitely on display and that increases your popularity no end. When it comes to the more practical aspects of life you have what it takes to see a particularly ticklish job through to its conclusion and you can make a new friend on the way. Virgo is now more likely to bend with the wind when necessary.

10 FRIDAY   *Moon Age Day 14   Moon Sign Leo*

This is a time to make absolutely certain that things go according to plan. Second best won't be nearly good enough for you now and there are indications that you will go to tremendous trouble to get things absolutely right. All this effort should turn out to be very worthwhile and your popularity should rise at an incredible rate.

11 SATURDAY   *Moon Age Day 15   Moon Sign Leo*

You are anxious to promote greater security for the future – something that is nearly always on your mind in one way or another. Now you have the chance to look far ahead and to make decisions that are definitely going to favour you in the years to come. Socially, however, your mind is focused on the events of today.

12 SUNDAY   *Moon Age Day 16   Moon Sign Virgo*

The Moon is back in your sign and this could prove to be the most dynamic start to a new week you have experienced so far this year. The lunar high makes you slightly more aggressive, enabling you to easily get what you want from life. Lady Luck is likely to be working on your behalf today and tomorrow.

13 MONDAY
Moon Age Day 17   Moon Sign Virgo

Keep up your efforts because it really is worthwhile going that extra mile whilst the lunar high is supporting you. Even people you don't know very well at all are likely to be doing what they can for you and the impression you make on the world is so great that hardly anyone can fail to notice or admire you in some way.

14 TUESDAY
Moon Age Day 18   Moon Sign Libra

It will seem to be very important to you today to be high in the estimation of people with whom you work and live. It doesn't matter who is looking at you – you still want them to have a good impression. Actually you don't have to worry because as a Virgo you are generally respected, at work, at home and socially.

15 WEDNESDAY
Moon Age Day 19   Moon Sign Libra

The greatest opportunities for advancement are now in the area of your work, but this doesn't mean you should forget about your social life, which is also looking fairly good right now. All in all you should be generally happy with your lot, though you might have to work hard for the next few days if you want to be better off.

16 THURSDAY
Moon Age Day 20   Moon Sign Libra

The planetary focus turns to romance today and your personal relationships should be going very well. There is plenty of time to cultivate new interests and you should be quite inspirational in your approach to work. If one way of doing things doesn't work you can now quickly dream up something quite different.

17 FRIDAY
Moon Age Day 21   Moon Sign Scorpio

Take the opportunity to catch up on minor tasks. Your level of patience is even greater than it usually is and you will be especially good when dealing with people who are having difficulty coming to terms with confusing situations. You are a natural teacher at the moment and people will turn to you for help.

18 SATURDAY
Moon Age Day 22   Moon Sign Scorpio

Routines won't bother you but neither will those occasions when you have to be different and inspirational in order to get things done. Your level of confidence remains generally high and you may discover abilities you didn't really know you had. A strong competitive edge begins to develop within you now.

19 SUNDAY
Moon Age Day 23   Moon Sign Sagittarius

Use this time to take stock of your affairs and to plan your strategy for further down the line. Get in touch with people you don't see often, answer emails, texts and letters and generally get caught up with minor tasks. Family-related issues can also be dealt with today because although you are quiet socially you are talking at home.

20 MONDAY
Moon Age Day 24   Moon Sign Sagittarius

Now you need to plan ahead carefully and to control your personal budget in a slightly different way. You also have your detective head on at present and will be very keen to do whatever you can to find out how everything works. Turning your practical skills to getting things done is what really makes the difference now.

21 TUESDAY
Moon Age Day 25   Moon Sign Sagittarius

Personal happiness should surround you now. Relationships look good and past issues that have upset the applecart can now be left behind you once and for all. Certain changes you had been planning may no longer be necessary and you may enjoy the feeling that you can settle down in some way.

22 WEDNESDAY
Moon Age Day 26   Moon Sign Capricorn

You have a sharp wit and have much mental energy. This is likely to find its way out in a number of different ways but it's clear you would be good at word games, puzzles and quizzes. Friends have a great deal to say to you at present and will offer all manner of advice, some of which is actually worth listening to seriously.

23 THURSDAY
Moon Age Day 27   Moon Sign Capricorn

Valuable influences now surround you when it comes to your personal finances and you will be quite keen to explore new avenues in order to increase your available cash. Maybe you will take on a part-time job or find other ways to add to the pile of coins you keep hidden somewhere. Plan ahead for holidays.

24 FRIDAY
Moon Age Day 28   Moon Sign Aquarius

Some conflict at work is to be expected around this time, probably because you find it more difficult to agree with colleagues or to accept that their way of doing things is the right approach. In the end you will have to choose for yourself but it wouldn't do any harm to turn up the level of your diplomacy. That way you avoid confrontation.

25 SATURDAY
Moon Age Day 0   Moon Sign Aquarius

All family matters are of interest to you now. It looks as though personal attachments are the ones that will take up most of your thinking time and you can find ways and means to show your love and affection – albeit through ingenious strategies. In a more practical sense, get to grips with some new piece of machinery or equipment.

26 SUNDAY
Moon Age Day 1   Moon Sign Aquarius

If you are not careful there could once again be certain difficulties arising on the financial front. Maybe someone at home has been spending too lavishly or it could be that you are annoyed because you don't think you have recently got value for money. Whatever the problem might be you will want to get it sorted out quickly.

27 MONDAY
Moon Age Day 2   Moon Sign Pisces

Along comes the lunar low and you will be quite sure that everyone is doing better than you are. This is a constant theme at the moment but is made worse by the position of the Moon in your opposite sign of Pisces. Rest and relax, allowing situations to take their course without your intervention.

28 TUESDAY
Moon Age Day 3   Moon Sign Pisces

Expecting as little as possible might be the best attitude to adopt today, even though that might seem rather defeatist. Actually things are likely to turn out rather better than you might expect but if you don't look for too much you can't be disappointed. Rely on the good offices of colleagues and friends – as well as family members.

2017

Your Month at a Glance

⊕ = Opportunities are around   ● = Be on the defensive   ◯ = Life is pretty ordinary

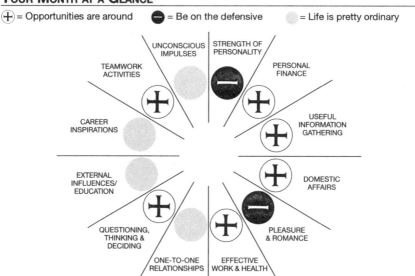

March Highs and Lows

Here I show you how the rhythms of the Moon will affect you this month. Like the tide, your energies and abilities will rise and fall with its pattern. When it is above the centre line, go for it, when it is below, you should be resting.

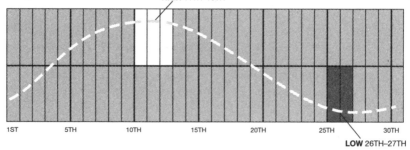

HIGH 11TH–13TH

1ST   5TH   10TH   15TH   20TH   25TH   30TH

LOW 26TH–27TH

58

1 WEDNESDAY
Moon Age Day 4   Moon Sign Aries

At the beginning of March it is important to clear any deadwood from your life. By lightening your load you are more likely to find the success you desire, whilst at the same time making life less complicated. See what you can do to make yourself more streamlined during the middle of this week.

2 THURSDAY
Moon Age Day 5   Moon Sign Aries

This is a time of boundless vitality and you have a greater need than usual to be on display. Virgo often relishes being in the background but that is certainly not going to be the case at present. Creative potential is especially good and you may also decide the time is right to make significant changes in at home.

3 FRIDAY
Moon Age Day 6   Moon Sign Taurus

Focus today on what makes you unique. You may attract a lot of attention by doing what seems natural to you. Being noticed is very important if you are presently looking for support in order to proceed with something you see as being very important. Don't allow family concerns or worries to get you down.

4 SATURDAY
Moon Age Day 7   Moon Sign Taurus

Practical matters will keep you generally busy and offer you with new incentives that keep the pot boiling as far as your life is concerned. This is certainly no time to be standing still or to be relying too heavily on the good offices of others. In the main you need to help yourself at the moment and won't be content to be a passenger.

5 SUNDAY
Moon Age Day 8   Moon Sign Gemini

You know what you want and should have a fairly good idea how to get it. There are some strong and very supportive planetary trends around right now, all of which are telling you to proceed when you see a green light in your mind. A Virgo is never happy when tied down by restrictive routines.

6 MONDAY
Moon Age Day 9   Moon Sign Gemini

Cutting through the red tape and getting to the essentials in life can be very important right now, and you won't be at all happy if you get yourself stuck in some cul-de-sac or other instead of moving forward progressively. You may have to be quite ruthless in order to get what you want from others but the end could justify the means.

7 TUESDAY
Moon Age Day 10   Moon Sign Cancer

Today is the time for action and for taking all those observations and thoughts of the last few days and making them work to your advantage. Colleagues should prove to be very helpful at work and friends are especially co-operative later. Don't sit in the background but make yourself a valuable part of life.

8 WEDNESDAY
Moon Age Day 11   Moon Sign Cancer

It's true that you are thinking about number one a great deal more now than would usually be the case but on the other hand you can't really help others to get on unless things are working properly for you. This isn't selfishness, merely the normal Virgo desire to make things turn out to your preordained pattern.

9 THURSDAY
Moon Age Day 12   Moon Sign Leo

Your personal finances should be gradually improving and if they are not you need to work harder and plan more fully. If there is one thing Virgo hates it is to be without money and a great deal of energy is always given to future securities. Listen to a friend who has a quite amazing idea. It needs modifying – but it could be fun.

10 FRIDAY
Moon Age Day 13   Moon Sign Leo

You can do much to make this a very special day, both for yourself and for those you care about the most. Stand aloof from any sort of argument that is taking place around you and where possible play the honest broker. Not that there is that much time for conciliation. You are now progressive, determined and enthusiastic.

11 SATURDAY
Moon Age Day 14   Moon Sign Virgo

Today you should find most of your personal aims easy to achieve. You won't want to sit around for long at a time because there are things to do, people to see and endless possibilities to exploit. Whether you will manage to achieve everything you want remains to be seen but one thing is certain – you will have a very good try.

12 SUNDAY
Moon Age Day 15   Moon Sign Virgo

This is the time for getting ahead faster and more capably than at any other stage during the last three or four weeks. With the new working week tomorrow comes a desire to exploit your potential to the full. Not only do you show great determination, you also exude charm to such an extent that nobody will refuse you any reasonable request.

13 MONDAY
Moon Age Day 16   Moon Sign Virgo

You can use all the energy you possess at the moment to build yourself a more interesting and varied social life. At the same time your romantic impulses tend to be very strong and if you are presently between relationships now could be the best time to tell someone special how you feel about them. Your popularity is assured.

14 TUESDAY
Moon Age Day 17   Moon Sign Libra

Remember that no matter how capable you may be there is a limit to what you can achieve on your own, which is why co-operating with others can be so important at the moment. Too many rules and regulations are likely to get on your nerves right now, which is why you want to fly free just as much as possible.

15 WEDNESDAY
Moon Age Day 18   Moon Sign Libra

It is a fact that you will get on best today when you sort things into little boxes and you will only come unstuck when you try to be too haphazard in the way you approach life generally. Virgo needs structure and although this can occasionally prove to be irritating to others, it is the way you have to be – though not all the time.

16 THURSDAY
Moon Age Day 19   Moon Sign Scorpio

This would be an excellent time for pioneering activities and for trying your hand at something completely new. The more you have to tax your mind, the better you are likely to feel and you are also quite physically motivated at the moment. Brand new plans and schemes are bound to be fed by your present state of mind.

17 FRIDAY
Moon Age Day 20   Moon Sign Scorpio

Communications are assisted by the present position of the Sun in your solar chart and you will be at your brightest and best when in almost any sort of company. It looks as though you can expect a few surprises today, one or two of which have something to do with your love life. In all practical matters you show yourself to be well organised.

18 SATURDAY
Moon Age Day 21   Moon Sign Scorpio

Let your mind wander a little during the weekend because within your imagination lies the forge where many of your future adventures are created. At the same time you should be active and willing to move around as much as possible. You might enjoy a shopping spree today and could find some real bargains.

19 SUNDAY
Moon Age Day 22   Moon Sign Sagittarius

Your natural love of detail stands you in good stead today. Whilst others get things approximately right you will only settle for perfection. This can make you a hard master to serve but everyone will be pleased with the results of your efforts. Expect some distractions at the moment, especially in terms of your social life.

20 MONDAY
Moon Age Day 23   Moon Sign Sagittarius

Original ideas and insights can advance your career. Try to step out of the groove and to be as free-spirited as possible. Of course you won't abandon your usual common sense and you will always work carefully towards your objectives. The only real difference is that for the moment you are slightly more adventurous.

21 TUESDAY
Moon Age Day 24   Moon Sign Capricorn

Certain curiosities have a part to play in your life under present trends and this could lead to some eyebrow-raising news in terms of your personal life. Once again it is important to make sure you are not wasting time on pointless distractions and, especially where money is concerned, you need to concentrate as much as you can.

22 WEDNESDAY
Moon Age Day 25   Moon Sign Capricorn

It is towards intellectual pursuits that you are now inclined to turn and this fact works well with the present state of the planets. In some ways you feel like retreating into your shell but will be less likely to do so if you are in the company of people you know and trust. A significant romantic interlude is just around the corner.

23 THURSDAY
Moon Age Day 26   Moon Sign Capricorn

This is a time when you will actively choose to keep busy and to show everyone your most positive side. Not everyone will be on your side, even as far as your family is concerned, and a bit of coaxing could be necessary. Most of your responses are extremely good and you communicate better than ever.

24 FRIDAY
Moon Age Day 27   Moon Sign Aquarius

Your home is likely to be the scene for friendly gatherings around this time. It is possible that friends you don't see too often will now be showing up again and the arrival of the spring weather will make you feel more like getting out into the garden to tidy things up. Drop the responsibility a little and take note of the world.

25 SATURDAY
Moon Age Day 28   Moon Sign Aquarius

Beneficial family influences tend to continue and there is no doubt that this forms the centre of the most important trends surrounding you at the moment. You care very deeply for those closest to you and should be going through a very romantic and quite emotional phase. Finding the right words to express your love is easier now.

26 SUNDAY
Moon Age Day 29   Moon Sign Pisces

The lunar low finds you somewhat quieter, less committed to the change that is gradually becoming such an important part of your life and more inclined to sit back and watch. Actually there's nothing wrong with taking a well-earned break. It's not as if you are miserable and the world keeps turning, even without your help.

27 MONDAY
Moon Age Day 0   Moon Sign Pisces

Another fairly quiet day can be expected but that doesn't mean your mind stops working. You are watching, waiting and planning, so that by the time Tuesday arrives you will be ready to act more decisively that you have done so far this month. Anything you do or say today socially is likely to be fairly low-key.

28 TUESDAY
Moon Age Day 1   Moon Sign Aries

When it comes to vital personal projects, this is the best time to sort things out and to begin again if necessary. You stand at the edge of a very fortunate time and all that is required is your usual patience and your conviction regarding your own strengths. Routines can be a bind today but being a Virgo you do need them.

29 WEDNESDAY
Moon Age Day 2   Moon Sign Aries

You should find yourself in the midst of very interesting company during the middle of this working week. Whether you are committed to professional matters or doing what suits you, there are individuals around at present who can help you greatly. You will also be extremely curious today and you want to know how everything works.

30 THURSDAY
Moon Age Day 3   Moon Sign Taurus

Sudden events and slight reversals of fortune can take you by surprise today. This is partly because you are not reacting as positively or quickly as usual. If you do feel down in the dumps, lift your spirits by remembering that things will turn around after a couple of days. Try not to be glum.

31 FRIDAY
Moon Age Day 4   Moon Sign Taurus

You need to be busy and active today, not only for your own sake but also on account of the people who are depending on you. As a result it won't take long for any cobwebs to blow away and for you to feel absolutely on form. Try to achieve a positive balance today between the necessities of life and your personal desire for relaxation.

April

2017

YOUR MONTH AT A GLANCE

(+) = Opportunities are around   ⊖ = Be on the defensive   = Life is pretty ordinary

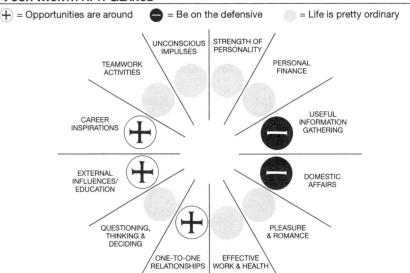

- UNCONSCIOUS IMPULSES
- STRENGTH OF PERSONALITY
- TEAMWORK ACTIVITIES
- PERSONAL FINANCE
- CAREER INSPIRATIONS (+)
- USEFUL INFORMATION GATHERING (−)
- EXTERNAL INFLUENCES/ EDUCATION (+)
- DOMESTIC AFFAIRS (−)
- QUESTIONING, THINKING & DECIDING (+)
- PLEASURE & ROMANCE
- ONE-TO-ONE RELATIONSHIPS
- EFFECTIVE WORK & HEALTH

APRIL HIGHS AND LOWS

Here I show you how the rhythms of the Moon will affect you this month. Like the tide, your energies and abilities will rise and fall with its pattern. When it is above the centre line, go for it, when it is below, you should be resting.

HIGH 8TH–9TH

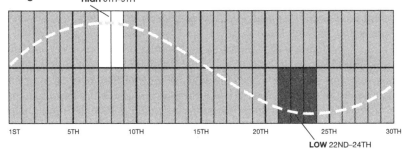

1ST   5TH   10TH   15TH   20TH   25TH   30TH

LOW 22ND–24TH

1 SATURDAY
Moon Age Day 5   Moon Sign Gemini

Although it might not be easy to get your point of view across today there are ways and means of doing so that you understand very well. You are an excellent people-watcher, especially at the moment. With everything to play for in the romance stakes this could turn out to be quite a time for some Virgos.

2 SUNDAY
Moon Age Day 6   Moon Sign Gemini

There may be a few sacrifices to be made today in order to please someone in the family or possibly a very good friend. That's no real hardship to you because you are very loyal and want the best for those you care about. Nothing will get in the way of a period of general good luck and happy situations.

3 MONDAY
Moon Age Day 7   Moon Sign Cancer

Aspects of your life that seemed to be a real problem only a week or two ago now seem to be resolving themselves, almost without any intervention from you. Life is better and you will also find a great many people to be especially helpful. There's no magic involved, it's simply a more optimistic outlook coming from you.

4 TUESDAY
Moon Age Day 8   Moon Sign Cancer

Social and teamwork matters are favourably highlighted and you shouldn't want for interesting company or a potentially good time. Keep an eye on your text messages and emails because there could be offers coming along right now that you won't want to miss. These may involve social invitations that sound especially appealing.

5 WEDNESDAY
Moon Age Day 9   Moon Sign Leo

The time is clearly right to go after what you want and there isn't much that is likely to stand in your way. The period has many high-points for Virgo people, not least of all in terms of personal and romantic possibilities. You tend to be quite acquisitive at the moment so purchases of one sort or another are very likely.

6 THURSDAY
Moon Age Day 10   Moon Sign Leo

Someone you don't see too often could be getting in touch, marking the start of a new emotional phase in your life but one that is far from negative. Everything seems bathed in sunshine for most Virgos at the moment, no matter what the weather is doing. Your ability to create opportunities is especially good.

7 FRIDAY
Moon Age Day 11   Moon Sign Leo

Make an early start with all practical matters and get jobs out of the way as and when they arise. If you follow this advice you will be ready when new and interesting possibilities come along and you won't have to keep other people waiting at all. You have a strong sense of justice right now when dealing with family matters.

8 SATURDAY
Moon Age Day 12   Moon Sign Virgo

Rely heavily on your intuitive strengths and make the weekend special by using the lunar high as a springboard. There is a real mix of possibilities around right now and you won't want to miss any of them. In particular you should find Lady Luck paying your life a visit and so although you don't usually gamble a small, measured flutter is likely.

9 SUNDAY
Moon Age Day 13   Moon Sign Virgo

The time is right to go for gold, though not necessarily the sort that can be kept in a bank vault or a jewellery box. Your strength of character is on display and you are so sure of yourself and your opinions that others simply go along with you as a matter of course. You call the shots today so think carefully what you really want.

10 MONDAY
Moon Age Day 14   Moon Sign Libra

The more diversity that comes your way at the moment, the greater will be your feelings of satisfaction. You may be pulled up in your tracks regarding some issues but that is a simple consequence of the Moon's position. When it matters the most you have what it takes to keep moving, and that's what really counts at the moment.

11 TUESDAY
Moon Age Day 15   Moon Sign Libra

A colleague or friend could be speaking quite highly of you and this acts as a tonic to make you even more confident and pleased with yourself and your recent efforts. You need these little presents from time to time because you are not always quite as certain of yourself as you appear to be. You could make a new friend now.

12 WEDNESDAY
Moon Age Day 16   Moon Sign Scorpio

It has never been easier to get along with your partner than it is now. You can make a real impact on them just by being what you naturally are – allied with perhaps a little more excitement that you sometimes generate. Keep abreast of current affairs and local news because both are going to be important soon.

13 THURSDAY ☿ *Moon Age Day 17   Moon Sign Scorpio*

When it comes to solving problems of almost any sort you are really in your element today. So keen are you on puzzles now that you will be actively seeking them out. Confidence is present in great measure when you are doing things you understand but is also possible when you are stretching yourself more than usual.

14 FRIDAY ☿ *Moon Age Day 18   Moon Sign Scorpio*

It's onward and upward in a general sense, with plenty of enthusiasm on your part and a greater desire than ever to get ahead. Many Virgoans will now be feeling energetic and even athletic – though it might be sensible to bear in mind your age before you over exert yourself! Your sense of humour is also highlighted.

15 SATURDAY ☿ *Moon Age Day 19   Moon Sign Sagittarius*

Things should continue to go well for you and there are few restrictions to report in a planetary sense. This might be a good time to get to grips with an issue that has been on your mind for a while. Things that may have seemed impossible only a few weeks ago now take on a completely different complexion. Keep nudging forward.

16 SUNDAY ☿ *Moon Age Day 20   Moon Sign Sagittarius*

Certain everyday discussions now seem to have plenty of cut and thrust and you won't have any difficulty at all letting others know the way you feel about things generally. There is just a slight possibility that you could end up getting involved in arguments whether you want to or not and this is something to avoid.

17 MONDAY ☿ *Moon Age Day 21   Moon Sign Capricorn*

You are likely to enjoy co-operation and harmony in your working life and it is outside of your own domain that you find the best aspects of your life playing out at the moment. Today is favourable for all public appearances and for making a good impression on bosses. More of your talents are now being appreciated.

18 TUESDAY ☿ *Moon Age Day 22   Moon Sign Capricorn*

Don't risk overturning already favourable situations by tampering too much. When something works well it probably isn't worth trying to establish why it does. It could still be rather easy to fall out with others and there is just a slight tendency for you to be bullish in some of your approaches. Play down a tendency to always know best.

19 WEDNESDAY ☿   *Moon Age Day 23   Moon Sign Capricorn*

You need to express your caring nature in very tangible ways, rather than simply expecting others to understand the way you feel. You are confident when you need to be and there are new incentives coming along all the time. It might seem to take an age to get through a tedious job but the earlier you start the sooner it will be done.

20 THURSDAY   ☿   *Moon Age Day 24   Moon Sign Aquarius*

Influential or important people now give you the support you need to do something quite amazing. Old prejudices are left behind and you will be far less inclined to live in the past than has sometimes been the case so far this month. People find you easy to deal with and your own level of personal confidence is clearly growing.

21 FRIDAY   ☿   *Moon Age Day 25   Moon Sign Aquarius*

There may be significant boosts to your ego around now. These are much more likely to have a bearing on your personal and romantic life than on practical situations. You will be in the market for new forms of entertainment and could lead the field when it comes to interesting new departures. You will also be very curious at this time.

22 SATURDAY   ☿   *Moon Age Day 26   Moon Sign Pisces*

The time has come to keep a slightly lower profile, though not for long. The lunar low will take the wind out of your sails a little but forewarned is forearmed. If you bear in mind that you probably won't be as energetic as usual and tackle jobs that are not too physically demanding, you may not notice the lunar low at all.

23 SUNDAY   ☿   *Moon Age Day 27   Moon Sign Pisces*

With the physical lull comes a certain acceptance that you will have to allow others to take some of the strain. Today can be lazy but lovely or it may seem distinctly frustrating. The choice is up to you. There really isn't any point in trying to move mountains on this particular Sunday but that doesn't mean you have to be miserable.

24 MONDAY   ☿   *Moon Age Day 28   Moon Sign Pisces*

There ought to be plenty of opportunity to do your own thing at this time and new initiatives are cropping up all the time. The only slight fly in the ointment is likely to be the attitude of friends and colleagues, which might be strange to say the least. Trying to get other people to do your bidding will not be easy but it should be interesting.

25 TUESDAY ☿ *Moon Age Day 0   Moon Sign Aries*

If there is one thing that you lack right now it is self-discipline. This is so unusual for Virgo that you could be stunned by your inability to stick to anything. Everyone needs to feel free sometimes, even you, and you can get a great deal of joy from simply living in the moment. There is enough time for a responsible attitude later.

26 WEDNESDAY ☿ *Moon Age Day 1   Moon Sign Aries*

A rather light-hearted period and an interlude during which you are happy to ring the changes throughout most of the day. There is just a slight possibility that someone else, probably your partner, will try to dominate your thinking and your actions. An adverse response is not necessary, but stay on your guard.

27 THURSDAY ☿ *Moon Age Day 2   Moon Sign Taurus*

Future prospects look extremely good and romance is especially rewarding at present. This part of the week can be one of both fun and of deep emotional attachments. It should be easy to express your feelings and you will also have a great desire to get away from restrictions and from the routines that inevitably have a bearing on your home life.

28 FRIDAY ☿ *Moon Age Day 3   Moon Sign Taurus*

This can be an extremely busy phase on the domestic front and if relatives are not easy to deal with you can at least be assured that life will be interesting. Relating to friends should be easier than understanding your loved ones, which is why you are more likely to socialise if the opportunity arises.

29 SATURDAY ☿ *Moon Age Day 4   Moon Sign Gemini*

You take your pleasures exactly where you find them today and won't be searching too much for fresh fields or pastures new. In any case there is plenty to keep you occupied in and around your own domain and with the better weather may come a desire to get on with practical matters. DIY could easily be on the cards today.

30 SUNDAY ☿ *Moon Age Day 5   Moon Sign Gemini*

Getting along well with others doesn't have to be a battle, though it might seem that way on occasion at the moment. Take heed of the fact that the more you listen to what is being said, the greater will be your own understanding. Avoid any tendency to defend yourself long before you have even been attacked.

2017

YOUR MONTH AT A GLANCE

⊕ = Opportunities are around   ⊖ = Be on the defensive   ◯ = Life is pretty ordinary

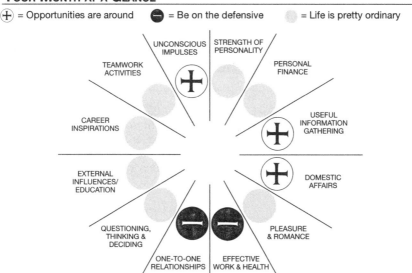

MAY HIGHS AND LOWS

Here I show you how the rhythms of the Moon will affect you this month. Like the tide, your energies and abilities will rise and fall with its pattern. When it is above the centre line, go for it, when it is below, you should be resting.

HIGH 5TH–6TH

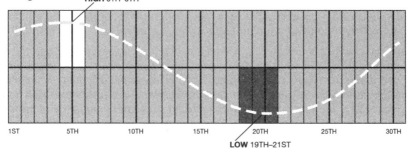

LOW 19TH–21ST

71

I MONDAY ☿   *Moon Age Day 6   Moon Sign Cancer*

Getting ahead might prove to be slightly difficult today, mainly because of the less-than-useful interventions of relatives or friends into your life. You could spend so much time sorting out other people that there simply are not enough moments left in which to shine. Never mind, at least you are storing up favours for later.

2 TUESDAY ☿   *Moon Age Day 7   Moon Sign Cancer*

An idealistic frame of mind might colour your opinions and actions between now and next week, which is fine just as long as your reforming zeal is kept slightly under control. For once not everything you are planning is exactly practical and you may have to turn to someone else in order to sort out troublesome little details.

3 WEDNESDAY ☿   *Moon Age Day 8   Moon Sign Leo*

Relationships can be doubly rewarding just now and you certainly won't want for good company at the moment. It's a two-way thing because you are giving as much to others as you get from them. For some Virgoans the time is now right to start a health regime but remember to take things steadily at first.

4 THURSDAY   *Moon Age Day 9   Moon Sign Leo*

Making too many compromises might be difficult, especially at work. The more stubborn side of your Earth-sign nature is showing and that means you will have to work that much harder in order to compromise. If you are shrewd you can find a way to at least let others think they are having a bigger input into situations than they actually are.

5 FRIDAY   *Moon Age Day 10   Moon Sign Virgo*

A little coercion may be required to get things working the way you want, and this comes easily because you are about as clever as you ever get. The lunar high should find you on top form and well able to address issues that have been something of a problem of late. Not only will you be extremely capable, your personality is charming and magnetic.

6 SATURDAY   *Moon Age Day 11   Moon Sign Virgo*

If ever there was a time to make the best of impressions on others, this is the day. From the moment you get out of bed until you crawl back into it again you are going to be on top form and well able to face almost any challenge. Even the state of your finances could be responding well to the presence of the Moon in its current position.

7 SUNDAY
Moon Age Day 12   Moon Sign Libra

The time is definitely right to remove some dead wood from your life. Virgo isn't the worst sign in the zodiac for hoarding things but is not the most streamlined either. Sometimes you find you are carrying so much baggage that you simply cannot make the progress you would wish. If this is the case now, consider what you don't need.

8 MONDAY
Moon Age Day 13   Moon Sign Libra

Make this a day for showing everyone what a kind and concerned individual you can be. Spend some time with family members and also make a special fuss of your partner or sweetheart. Do things that you know will please those around you and the chances are that you will have an excellent day yourself.

9 TUESDAY
Moon Age Day 14   Moon Sign Libra

Any obstacles that come along today are likely to have a bearing on the more practical and professional side of your life. These should be few and far between but they can exhaust you more than you might expect. Redress the balance by taking time out later to improve the quality and variety of your social life.

10 WEDNESDAY
Moon Age Day 15   Moon Sign Scorpio

You know yourself very well but perhaps not quite as completely as you think. Someone close to you could make a single remark today that will let you know just how well they understand the intricacies of your complicated nature. This realisation may not be earth shattering but it could pull you up in your tracks all the same.

11 THURSDAY
Moon Age Day 16   Moon Sign Scorpio

Positive highlights surround one-to-one relationships and you have what it takes to impress almost anyone. At the same time there is a depth to your nature that certain people may find fascinating and it might help if you deliberately cultivate the air of mystery you often seem to have. The desire for change increases.

12 FRIDAY
Moon Age Day 17   Moon Sign Sagittarius

Problems are best solved today using a high degree of intuition, together with a base of common sense, for which you are justifiably famous. If you find you are slightly depressed early in the day this is a situation you can turn round quickly by keeping busy and by finding ways to stretch your mind. Stay occupied and you will be happy.

13 SATURDAY
Moon Age Day 18   Moon Sign Sagittarius

It is your personal life and relationships that help to make your life more stable at present and you will be focusing a great deal of attention on romantic attachments. Virgo is red hot at present and if there is someone around you really want to impress wait until this evening, dress up and wow them.

14 SUNDAY
Moon Age Day 19   Moon Sign Sagittarius

If there is any dissatisfaction in your life right now it probably comes from not being able to follow your own path and in having to do what other people think is best. You are certainly likely to kick against authority today, especially if you see it as being pointless and restrictive. Virgo can sometimes feel like a caged animal.

15 MONDAY
Moon Age Day 20   Moon Sign Capricorn

An emotional issue might be difficult to solve and would be better off put on ice for the moment because in the end it could sort itself out. Not that you should ignore everything today. In a more practical sense you will need to intervene and to make sure that something at work is done to your personal satisfaction.

16 TUESDAY
Moon Age Day 21   Moon Sign Capricorn

You should enjoy a successful day as far as material considerations are concerned, even if you are slightly out of sorts with yourself on an emotional level. The forces of progress will be on your side and it is important to deal with issues as and when they arise. In terms of cash, do not leave things to chance.

17 WEDNESDAY
Moon Age Day 22   Moon Sign Aquarius

Your emotional needs require special recognition again at present and it might seem as though some of the people you should be able to rely upon are forgetting about you. Maybe that's because you don't let them know you are feeling vulnerable. In the midst of a busy life everyone is a little thoughtless occasionally.

18 THURSDAY
Moon Age Day 23   Moon Sign Aquarius

Though the control you have over your life at present is quite as complete as you would wish, when it really matters you genuinely will be the one making the decisions. If you feel that this is not the case it could be because you recognise your responsibility to others. Get together with like-minded people in community issues.

19 FRIDAY
Moon Age Day 24   Moon Sign Pisces

Slow everything down and look more carefully at the way you are undertaking some tasks. There are opposing planetary influences working on you right now, with some planets pushing you forward and the lunar low trying to hold you back. A little circumspection will be no bad thing, together with the chance to catch your breath.

20 SATURDAY
Moon Age Day 25   Moon Sign Pisces

Once again you are unlikely to be breaking any records in terms of what you get done but you can at least be happy in the thought that any job you decide to undertake will be done methodically. You may not feel as though you are scintillating company, but maybe you should leave the ultimate judgement to the people you meet?

21 SUNDAY
Moon Age Day 26   Moon Sign Pisces

You may feel that you need to get together with colleagues in order to avert what could be a difficult issue in the near future. You are very intuitive at the moment and tend to see ahead of yourself in a very clear way. Not everyone has this ability and it might take some persuasion on your part to make others appreciate your wisdom.

22 MONDAY
Moon Age Day 27   Moon Sign Aries

Now is the time to really take the lead where major plans and operations are concerned. People will quite naturally follow your lead and all it takes from you is a word to have everyone falling in line. Money matters are likely to be strong and there are newer and better ways to help your life run smoothly.

23 TUESDAY
Moon Age Day 28   Moon Sign Aries

There are some good ideas coming your way, some of which arise out of past experiences allied to what is happening in your life at the moment. Look for useful input that comes from the direction of your friends and also take time out to be with family members. Most important of all, let your partner know how much you care.

24 WEDNESDAY
Moon Age Day 29   Moon Sign Taurus

There are rewards on the way for Virgoans who are willing to put themselves out. Today won't bring much if you simply sit and wait, but put in that extra bit of effort and just see what happens. Don't settle for your usual midweek routines but shake life up and make it produce what you are really wanting.

25 THURSDAY
Moon Age Day 0   Moon Sign Taurus

Issues on the domestic front could become unsettled and relationships might seem slightly top heavy. This is because you are taking your eye off the ball. Although you will have plenty to keep you occupied outside your home, you still need to find time to confront potentially difficult issues. Nip these in the bud and all should be well.

26 FRIDAY
Moon Age Day 1   Moon Sign Gemini

Be on the lookout to make contact with people you haven't seen for ages, as well as making yourself aware of the newcomers who are turning up in your social life especially. This is a day when the past is reflected in the present and a time when you have the chance to make comparisons. Be scrupulously truthful in everything now.

27 SATURDAY
Moon Age Day 2   Moon Sign Gemini

If you happen to work at the weekend you could be one of the luckiest of Virgoans today. It is towards business that trends are taking you, so that even if you do not have to toil away today you will still be mulling things over. Advancement could be on the way, together with exciting new responsibilities.

28 SUNDAY
Moon Age Day 3   Moon Sign Cancer

Someone in your immediate circle is likely to seem quite discouraging but the fact is they do have your best interests at heart. This is why you should not upset them by directly going against their advice. There are ways and means of following your own plans without making it plain you are refusing sound advice.

29 MONDAY
Moon Age Day 4   Moon Sign Cancer

Plans that are now on the drawing board should move ahead progressively and there doesn't seem to be too much to get in your way. At the start of the day it might seem as though you are up against a mountain of work but because you are so efficient at present you will get through much of it in a fraction of the expected time.

30 TUESDAY
Moon Age Day 5   Moon Sign Leo

You have a good intuitive understanding of the people who surround you at the moment and won't have any real difficulty working out what makes them tick. What a pity they are not quite as responsive to you. You have what it takes to be at your best in social settings and will enjoy anything new or slightly off the wall this evening.

31 WEDNESDAY
Moon Age Day 6   Moon Sign Leo

When it comes to leisure and pleasure you are really on the ball today. Although you will still be fulfilling your obligations in a general sense you will also be finding new things to do. These may have no practical purpose and simply exist for the sake of enjoyment. Not everything at this time has to have a reason – simply accept it.

2017

YOUR MONTH AT A GLANCE

⊕ = Opportunities are around   ⊖ = Be on the defensive   ⦿ = Life is pretty ordinary

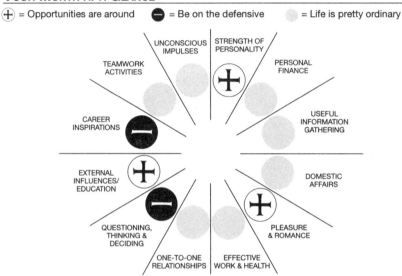

JUNE HIGHS AND LOWS

Here I show you how the rhythms of the Moon will affect you this month. Like the tide, your energies and abilities will rise and fall with its pattern. When it is above the centre line, go for it, when it is below, you should be resting.

HIGH 1ST–3RD   **HIGH** 29TH–30TH

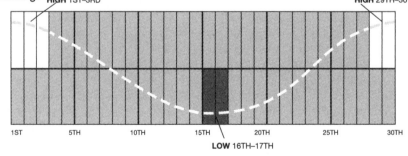

1ST   5TH   10TH   15TH   20TH   25TH   30TH

LOW 16TH–17TH

78

1 THURSDAY
Moon Age Day 7   Moon Sign Virgo

Today could turn out to be one of the luckiest days of the month, which is why you need to be up and about early and putting creative ideas to the test. Opportunities are out there just waiting for you and there are messages coming along from some very unlikely directions. It might be worth taking a few calculated risks just now.

2 FRIDAY
Moon Age Day 8   Moon Sign Virgo

You enjoy a very high profile and your power to have a pronounced bearing on your own life and its circumstances is extremely strong. You are so filled with a positive life force that others are instantly and instinctively attracted to you. Expect a few strange but fortunate coincidences and see situations for what they really are.

3 SATURDAY
Moon Age Day 9   Moon Sign Virgo

There is plenty of support around today but you may often fail to recognise it. It is towards the social aspects of life that you need to turn, whilst allowing more practical matters to wait for a while. Think things through by all means but don't spend too much time weighing up the pros and cons. Actions speak loudest.

4 SUNDAY
Moon Age Day 10   Moon Sign Libra

The social scene should be fairly interesting and could introduce you to people you haven't known well before but who are likely to become increasingly important in the days ahead. Stand by for a few weird events, though none of these are likely to work against your best interests. Be sure to keep all confidences right now.

5 MONDAY
Moon Age Day 11   Moon Sign Libra

It would be a good idea to vary your routines as much as possible at the start of this week and you need to be especially flexible in your general attitude. This isn't always easy for you but you should remember that a tree that bends in the wind is far less likely to break. Friends should be reliable but maybe a little mad on occasions.

6 THURSDAY
Moon Age Day 12   Moon Sign Scorpio

You continue to plough into life in a very positive way and you should be enjoying yourself a lot. Anything you love to do is likely to be easier and better under prevailing planetary trends and you exude joy when in social settings. Not everyone loves you at the moment but almost all those people who matter certainly do.

7 WEDNESDAY
Moon Age Day 13   Moon Sign Scorpio

It is likely that you will now shy away from anything too routine or run of the mill. There are advantages to be had from rushing in where angels fear to tread, if only because nobody expects it from you. All in all this could turn out to be one of the most successful and financially sound periods of the year so far.

8 THURSDAY
Moon Age Day 14   Moon Sign Sagittarius

There are some very charming people around at the moment and you should be encountering a broad cross-section of individuals who you will instinctively take to. Because you are more communicative than is sometimes the case you are in the best possible position to ask for things you either need or want. The response should be good.

9 FRIDAY
Moon Age Day 15   Moon Sign Sagittarius

You should continue to get a little more from life than you generally expect but a great deal is presently down to your own attitude and actions. This is certainly no time to hold back or to be over modest. People generally want you to get on well and will be doing all they can to support you, and it is very important to realise this.

10 SATURDAY
Moon Age Day 16   Moon Sign Sagittarius

Life's tempo quickens again by a few paces but you will probably still have the feeling that you are working predominantly to make other people happier. There's nothing too wrong with that, unless of course you feel that certain individuals should be doing more to help themselves. You may feel obliged to impart a few home truths.

11 SUNDAY
Moon Age Day 17   Moon Sign Capricorn

Find out what is going on beyond the limits of your own private world and opt to get involved. It may be that you are drawn into local or regional issues of one sort or another or that you find something out about your locality that is particularly fascinating. Your commitment to romance is especially strong at this time.

12 MONDAY
Moon Age Day 18   Moon Sign Capricorn

You enter a new working week with a great deal of enthusiasm and energy, only to find that on a few occasions things are not working out quite as you anticipated. This is when you need to be original in your thinking and to roll with the punches. Nothing really untoward is likely to happen and life remains generally favourable.

13 TUESDAY
Moon Age Day 19   Moon Sign Aquarius

What happens today, either culturally or socially, could quite easily lead towards some enlivening experiences. Anything old or curious will really captivate your imagination and the more refined side of your nature is clearly on display. Leave all dirty or unsavoury jobs until another time and simply enjoy the finer things of life.

14 WEDNESDAY
Moon Age Day 20   Moon Sign Aquarius

Avoid oversights by concentrating on specifics but leave alone all matters that have nothing at all to do with you personally. You remain basically active and enterprising, though you might occasionally show that stubborn side of your nature that can be such a stumbling block. It is vital that you continue to demonstrate flexibility.

15 THURSDAY
Moon Age Day 21   Moon Sign Aquarius

Today could easily be a time for examining intense personal relationships and a period during which love is uppermost in your mind. At the same time you will be quite busy at work and so there may not be a great deal of time to spare. It would be best to pace yourself and to enlist some support at times.

16 FRIDAY
Moon Age Day 22   Moon Sign Pisces

With the lunar low comes a definite desire to retreat into yourself and it might be difficult for others to really get onside with your deep and complex nature. The more you talk, the greater will be your own sense of satisfaction, not to mention the positive bearing it has on relationships. Avoid getting depressed about unimportant matters.

17 SATURDAY
Moon Age Day 23   Moon Sign Pisces

Rules and regulations continue to get on your nerves and the situation is exaggerated whilst the lunar low is around. You will kick against anything you see as being restrictive or pointless and yet in many cases you don't have a better idea. There's no point in arguing for the sake of doing so and maybe you are just being plain awkward.

18 SUNDAY
Moon Age Day 24   Moon Sign Aries

The happy times should continue unabated. Actually not much has changed but since you have emerged from a distinctly introspective period everything should look light and airy. The summer has arrived so make the most of it by getting out of the house today – even if it's only as far as your garden.

19 MONDAY
Moon Age Day 25   Moon Sign Aries

Romantic and social matters are positively highlighted, though you will insist on being number one in at least some of your exploits. Don't get tied down with pointless details, which is something that tends to happen to Virgoans from time to time. Cut through red tape as if you were carrying a very large pair of scissors.

20 TUESDAY
Moon Age Day 26   Moon Sign Taurus

You seem to have the best of both worlds at the moment. Both your work and the social scene look good and it should be more than possible to mix business with pleasure. There are some positive planetary highlights on the way and you shine best when in good company. Stick with long-term friends.

21 WEDNESDAY
Moon Age Day 27   Moon Sign Taurus

You clearly prefer your own company and will want to keep away from large crowds for the moment. This doesn't apply in the case of people you already know and in any case it is their presence that makes things go so well. Virgo is deeply intellectual at this time and extremely curious about anything and everything.

22 THURSDAY
Moon Age Day 28   Moon Sign Gemini

Romantic matters could provide your most interesting moments today and you are probably exploring the softer side of your nature. There may be a natural tendency to avoid getting involved in anything too complicated and there is just a slight tendency for you to retreat into your own little world on occasions.

23 FRIDAY
Moon Age Day 29   Moon Sign Gemini

When it comes to professional endeavours the advice today is to get cracking ahead of the weekend. You can finish this particular working week on a real high and could be quite staggered by your own success. A little cheek goes a long way and you can get something that is quite important to you by simply having the nerve to ask for it.

24 SATURDAY
Moon Age Day 0   Moon Sign Cancer

You now bring out the best in others by highlighting their good points. People will be more than happy to have you around and it could be difficult to keep up with all the invitations that are coming your way. There is a growing need for change on your part and you will relish any chance to take a journey.

25 SUNDAY · Moon Age Day 1 · Moon Sign Cancer

A shift in the direction of greater communication is indicated and you will continue to find yourself in extremely good company. It isn't that others are persuading you to talk all the time – it's just the way the planets are arranged for you at the moment. This is a very good time to get something you really want.

26 MONDAY · Moon Age Day 2 · Moon Sign Leo

Positive highlights are on the way in terms of new friendships – a trend that in one way or another is going to be with you for the next few weeks. For some Virgos there is also a chance of new romance and an ability to wow someone you might have thought was well beyond your reach. Stay optimistic, happy and smart.

27 TUESDAY · Moon Age Day 3 · Moon Sign Leo

Making just the right sort of progress should turn out to be child's play at the moment. Mercury is now in a good position for you and allows you to get your message across in a slightly more diplomatic way than might have been the case over the last few days. People find you good to have around and the social invitations roll in.

28 WEDNESDAY · Moon Age Day 4 · Moon Sign Leo

In partnerships you are looking for intellectual stimulation and this reflects in your romantic life. What you want from your partner is mental support and the feeling that you are both on the same wavelength. At work you could be slightly more thoughtful and less inclined to take a chance on something you consider to be potentially difficult.

29 THURSDAY · Moon Age Day 5 · Moon Sign Virgo

A phase of increased personal magnetism can be expected which makes this a good time for business dealings and for getting to grips with thorny issues you have been avoiding. Your level of luck should be increased and you will be very popular when it company. It looks as though your mental processes will be well honed.

30 FRIDAY · Moon Age Day 6 · Moon Sign Virgo

You could now make headway with money and you are likely to be on top form. With everything to play for in the romantic stakes you once again prove just how amorous and approachable you can be. It is the material side of life that is best supported by the lunar high but you will also be shining like a star socially.

2017

YOUR MONTH AT A GLANCE

⊕ = Opportunities are around   ⊖ = Be on the defensive   ▓ = Life is pretty ordinary

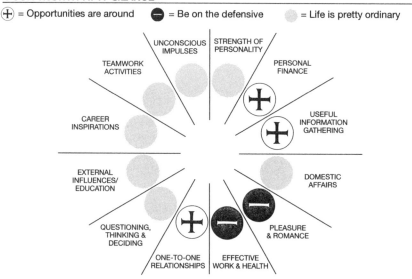

UNCONSCIOUS IMPULSES

STRENGTH OF PERSONALITY

TEAMWORK ACTIVITIES

PERSONAL FINANCE

CAREER INSPIRATIONS

USEFUL INFORMATION GATHERING

EXTERNAL INFLUENCES/ EDUCATION

DOMESTIC AFFAIRS

QUESTIONING, THINKING & DECIDING

PLEASURE & ROMANCE

ONE-TO-ONE RELATIONSHIPS

EFFECTIVE WORK & HEALTH

JULY HIGHS AND LOWS

Here I show you how the rhythms of the Moon will affect you this month. Like the tide, your energies and abilities will rise and fall with its pattern. When it is above the centre line, go for it, when it is below, you should be resting.

HIGH 26TH–27TH

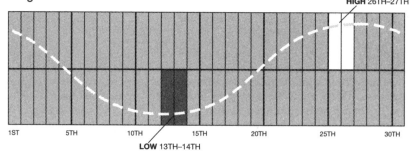

1ST   5TH   10TH   15TH   20TH   25TH   30TH

LOW 13TH–14TH

1 SATURDAY   *Moon Age Day 7   Moon Sign Libra*

There may be unusual and exciting social possibilities to be taken into account today and although the Moon has now moved out of Virgo that doesn't mean that your run of good luck is over. You are pretty much in charge of your own destiny at the moment and won't take very kindly to anyone telling you what to do.

2 SUNDAY   *Moon Age Day 8   Moon Sign Libra*

Maybe it would be just as well if others didn't expect you to be assertive today because you are likely to have entered a somewhat quieter spell. This is unlikely to last long but in any case there is nothing particularly strange about a somewhat withdrawn Virgo. You merely need some time to yourself.

3 MONDAY   *Moon Age Day 9   Moon Sign Scorpio*

Though probably still socially reluctant you will be coming out of your shell somewhat when in the company of really good friends or long-term associates. Slowly but surely you begin to open up and put forward some definite ideas about the way things should be done. Routines may still suit you.

4 TUESDAY   *Moon Age Day 10   Moon Sign Scorpio*

Stand by for a new and more satisfying period and a time when you are once again back in command and happy to be out there in the social mainstream. No matter what the plans taking place around you, people will be pleased to have you on board because you always speak so much sense.

5 WEDNESDAY   *Moon Age Day 11   Moon Sign Scorpio*

If you find you are looking out at the world from behind your own self-made curtain today you can at least be assured that by tomorrow things should change significantly. Don't take it for granted that this particular period has nothing to recommend it. On the contrary your ability to look and plan ahead is good.

6 THURSDAY   *Moon Age Day 12   Moon Sign Sagittarius*

Today is excellent when it comes to pitching yourself into situations and making sure that things are work out to your advantage. You feel fully in charge of your life and happy to do whatever it takes to follow your objectives through to their logical conclusion. Friends are happy to impart confidences now.

7 FRIDAY
Moon Age Day 13   Moon Sign Sagittarius

With greater professional luck, a more solid base from which to work and plenty of know-how there is no reason why you should stick fast under present planetary trends. Everything seems to be setting itself up to offer you more of what you want, and at a personal price you feel you can afford. Hard work might be necessary but that's no problem.

8 SATURDAY
Moon Age Day 14   Moon Sign Capricorn

Emotional and domestic matters are on your mind, which probably isn't a bad thing on a Saturday. However, you still have a strong desire to do something exciting or even outrageous and there ought to be at least a few people around you who would be happy to join in with. Whatever you decide, make sure you plan your strategy well.

9 SUNDAY
Moon Age Day 15   Moon Sign Capricorn

If you have to challenge others at the moment try to do so with a little tact and diplomacy. There is just a chance that you are so keen to speak your mind that you will forget you are dealing with other human beings, some of whom may in any case be too sensitive for their own good. Softly, softly is the best approach for now.

10 MONDAY
Moon Age Day 16   Moon Sign Capricorn

Your charm is noteworthy and your ideas are impressive. All you need now is an audience and life itself may take care of issues on your behalf. It looks as though you are going to be catapulted into the limelight – a place that might often be uncomfortable for a Virgo but which suits you well enough at the moment.

11 TUESDAY
Moon Age Day 17   Moon Sign Aquarius

You may strive to simplify matters and to get things generally running the way you want today. There are some irritants about, not least of all the attitude and behaviour of friends, which is not what you would generally expect or wish. If you can't make the world what you want it to be, accept the fact and carry on.

12 WEDNESDAY
Moon Age Day 18   Moon Sign Aquarius

What you learn from others may have an effect on your behaviour today and element of caution is required. Accepting the adage that 'there is no smoke without fire' is fine as a rule but to do so now might mean you dangerously fail to understand the reason that situations are the way they are.

13 THURSDAY
Moon Age Day 19   Moon Sign Pisces

With the Moon now in Pisces you will probably find that you are happier to watch and wait for a couple of days, though there is definitely a battle going in inside you because you don't want to lose momentum with some of your plans. There is a middle way but that won't always be easy to find. Rely more on associates and friends.

14 FRIDAY
Moon Age Day 20   Moon Sign Pisces

It is the smallest and most apparently insignificant details of life that are likely to capture your attention and imagination for the moment and nothing is too tiny to escape your present level of scrutiny. Others find you hard to understand when in this frame of mind so you may think it best to soldier on alone.

15 SATURDAY
Moon Age Day 21   Moon Sign Aries

Although there are some people who will try your patience today it looks as though you are going to remain cool, calm and collected, no matter what. You take most situations very much in your stride and instead of getting annoyed when people irritate you there is a good chance that you will simply laugh and shrug it off.

16 SUNDAY
Moon Age Day 22   Moon Sign Aries

Look out for many different faces today because you get on better when mixing with a cross-section of people. Not everyone is going to be on your side but when the chips are down there are pals around who won't be found lacking. It is important to establish your particular point of view and then to stick to it.

17 MONDAY
Moon Age Day 23   Moon Sign Aries

There could be a few things to finish off at the start of this week – items that were left on hold last Friday. This means a significant commitment to work but not a great deal of apparent progress. The quiet side of your nature predominates, though almost certainly not for very long. By this evening you will be much more outgoing.

18 TUESDAY
Moon Age Day 24   Moon Sign Taurus

You are likely to enjoy travelling at this time and if you have planned a holiday for any time around now you have chosen wisely. So many different things arouse your curiosity and the present period should offer you the chance to discover something that will really make you sit up and think. You are in a caring mood now.

19 WEDNESDAY — *Moon Age Day 25   Moon Sign Taurus*

You could be reminded of various responsibilities today and you will want to let others know that you appreciate the way they have helped you out. For this reason much of today is likely to be spent repaying debts and catching up on necessary tasks. In amongst a busy time find moments for your partner.

20 THURSDAY — *Moon Age Day 26   Moon Sign Gemini*

Make the best of what's on offer at work but remember that there are also very good opportunities around associated with your social and personal life. It might not be easy to split your day equally but there are people around who can take up the reins of responsibility when you are not around. All work and no play is ever a good thing.

21 FRIDAY — *Moon Age Day 27   Moon Sign Gemini*

Today you are able to tackle jobs that require real discipline. It doesn't matter whether these form part of your working life or if there a social incentive involved. Your willingness to get things right is what really counts. People see you as capable and for this reason will be anxious to follow your lead.

22 SATURDAY — *Moon Age Day 28   Moon Sign Cancer*

Authorities of one sort or another and a mass of red tape are likely to stand between you and your chosen objectives today. There are two ways to deal with this situation. On the one hand you can lose your temper and achieve little or nothing; on the other you can use your wisdom and a little subterfuge in order to get what you want. You choose!

23 SUNDAY — *Moon Age Day 0   Moon Sign Cancer*

Inspirational conversations seem to be the order of the day. Not only are you in a good position to influence the decisions others are making you are also able to make a few of your own. All in all this should be an inspiring time and a period when you really feel that you can achieve great progress. Get on-side with new plans at home.

24 MONDAY — *Moon Age Day 1   Moon Sign Leo*

It is now very important for you to focus your energy and enthusiasm in specific directions. You have a great capacity for work but you could so easily dissipate all that positive energy by trying to do too much. Your competitive edge is stimulated and you will also be in the market for stepping up your romantic side.

25 TUESDAY
Moon Age Day 2   Moon Sign Leo

Your relationships are now very intense and there certainly won't be a better part of the month for romance than now. Contact with the people you love could lead to inner growth and there are gains to be made from expressing your affection in positive ways. You should be feeling far less shy than usual.

26 WEDNESDAY
Moon Age Day 3   Moon Sign Virgo

You have looked, waited and schemed and now whatever has been on your mind can be exploited to the full. There are gains to be made in your financial life but most important of all are the personal possibilities. You can attract others without really trying and the force of your personality is not lost on anyone today.

27 THURSDAY
Moon Age Day 4   Moon Sign Virgo

This is the best day of the month during which to put your luck to the test. With a great sense of your own potential and a desire to break down barriers you are probably more dynamic and potentially successful today than at any time during July. What a great time this would be to anticipate the start of a holiday.

28 FRIDAY
Moon Age Day 5   Moon Sign Libra

You can afford to be fairly optimistic, not because of what you are doing now but on account of moves you made in the recent past. It's as though everything comes together in the most positive way and you can think about a period of growth that you know lies ahead. Once again you are also responsive to romantic overtures.

29 SATURDAY
Moon Age Day 6   Moon Sign Libra

The world seems to make significant demands of you today but you take this in your stride. You can afford to back your hunches to a much greater extent than has been the case during the last week or so and should be on top form when in public situations. You might even surprise yourself with some of your positive responses.

30 SUNDAY
Moon Age Day 7   Moon Sign Libra

Everything seems to conspire at the moment to make you easy to know and responsive to the needs of others. It just so happens that lots of people will be on the same wavelength, which in turn encourages a greater degree of co-operation and ultimate success. Virgo remains in quite a romantic mood right now.

31 MONDAY
Moon Age Day 8   Moon Sign Scorpio

Your real forte at the moment lies in relating to others on a one-to-one basis. This might not always be a romantic response but there isn't much doubt that you have great popularity and you could have secret admirers. Don't be in the least surprised today if you are singled out for special treatment and take this in your stride.

2017

Your Month at a Glance

(+) = Opportunities are around   − = Be on the defensive   = Life is pretty ordinary

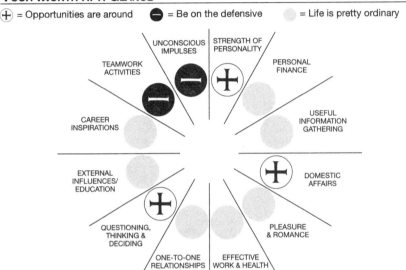

August Highs and Lows

Here I show you how the rhythms of the Moon will affect you this month. Like the tide, your energies and abilities will rise and fall with its pattern. When it is above the centre line, go for it, when it is below, you should be resting.

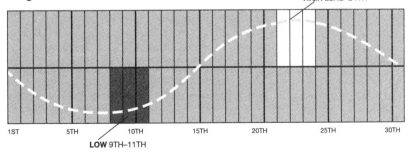

91

1 TUESDAY
Moon Age Day 9   Moon Sign Scorpio

The first day of August is all about resolving a personal matter, though a few of your desires could be quite unrealistic and some sound common sense is clearly called for at this time. Important matters are going to be left up in the air unless you decide on a little personal intervention. Everything today depends on getting involved.

2 WEDNESDAY
Moon Age Day 10   Moon Sign Sagittarius

Your routines at work may be affected by minor mishaps, though not if you concentrate on what you are doing. There's a good chance you will be interrupted repeatedly today by people who don't seem to know what they are doing and who call upon your help. Socially speaking things should be getting more interesting.

3 THURSDAY
Moon Age Day 11   Moon Sign Sagittarius

Organising yourself is always important but seems to be especially so right now, maybe because those with whom you live and work are so haphazard in what they are doing. You might be slightly nervy or inclined to snap at people but if this is the case you can rest assured that these trends are slight and that they won't last long.

4 FRIDAY
Moon Age Day 12   Moon Sign Sagittarius

You might have to put some distance between yourself and a friendship that was once very important to you. Times are changing for many Virgoans and you can't expect attachments to stay exactly the same. For some there will be a little pain in a parting but what comes further down the line will make this worthwhile.

5 SATURDAY
Moon Age Day 13   Moon Sign Capricorn

Minor, possibly unexpected, pressures can arise around now and these will take up a good deal of your time during the weekend. That doesn't mean you fail to enjoy yourself or to show what you are made of. On the contrary, it is when you are faced with having to make instant decisions that you are at your best.

6 SUNDAY
Moon Age Day 14   Moon Sign Capricorn

Your practical skills are excellent today and there isn't anyone in the zodiac that is more capable than you are at this time. Things that take others ages are done in a second and you have all you need to impress even the most important people. Some Virgos can expect some professional advancement soon.

7 MONDAY
Moon Age Day 15   Moon Sign Aquarius

There are satisfying results coming along for those of you who are willing to do that extra bit to finish something off. As one phase of your life starts to come to an end, so new possibilities are all around you. Working out exactly what you are going to do next will form part of the excitement that comes later in August for you.

8 TUESDAY
Moon Age Day 16   Moon Sign Aquarius

Pace yourself today but make sure you get plenty of variety or you will soon become bored with routines. You are not exactly competitive right now but you do need to feel that you are 'taking part' in some way. Maybe you should be doing all the organising if you want to ensure a different and stimulating evening.

9 WEDNESDAY
Moon Age Day 17   Moon Sign Pisces

It could seem as though you are walking through treacle today. It isn't that you fail to get things done, merely that to do so takes so much longer than usual. With the lunar low also comes a sense of foreboding and a tendency to be rather gloomy for no apparent reason. Tell yourself this is just a phase – because that's the truth.

10 THURSDAY
Moon Age Day 18   Moon Sign Pisces

Energy remains in fairly short supply but as long as you don't expect to do everything yourself there is no reason why today should be inherently worse than any other. Be willing to watch and wait – which let's face it you are quite good at doing. Only if you are certain of yourself should you make any far-reaching decisions today.

11 FRIDAY
Moon Age Day 19   Moon Sign Pisces

You are very creative and may be indulging in new hobbies or pastimes. That's fine but it may not be enough at a time when you sense excitement around every new corner. Don't hold back when you are in social settings and be willing to express your opinions, even if to do so makes you slightly nervous.

12 SATURDAY
Moon Age Day 20   Moon Sign Aries

Certain friendships have a lot going for them today and you may want to pursue an idea that seemed done and finished but which has now gained a new lease of life. Enlist the support of those you trust, and learn to lean on someone you have been wary of before. There are great lessons to be learned around this time.

13 SUNDAY ☿   *Moon Age Day 21   Moon Sign Aries*

A little confusion on the part of a friend acts as an early warning to you that they need your help. You are likely to be on hand to assist almost anyone whose life is not going according to plan. At the same time you have what it takes to keep things ticking along nicely for you, especially in a financial sense.

14 MONDAY ☿   *Moon Age Day 22   Moon Sign Taurus*

Your competitive attitude in many spheres of your life this week can get you a long way but maybe you are being just a little too competitive for your own good in some respects. Allow others to do their part too and don't monopolise tasks that are not really yours to undertake. You should be especially good with money this week.

15 TUESDAY ☿   *Moon Age Day 23   Moon Sign Taurus*

This should be a first class time in a professional sense, though maybe slightly less gilt-edged with regard to the personal aspects of life. That wonderful, special touch that you have been exhibiting a lot this year is likely to be missing for a few days so take care that you do not come across as unfeeling.

16 WEDNESDAY ☿   *Moon Age Day 24   Moon Sign Gemini*

Your approach at work is now likely to be slightly more impatient than usual, but that is because you recognise that other people are not fulfilling their obligations towards you. There isn't much point in reacting strongly to anything because you get more of what you want when you show quiet restraint.

17 THURSDAY ☿   *Moon Age Day 25   Moon Sign Gemini*

Input and information is all-important today. There are many people around you with interesting things to say and if you listen to what they are telling you it is possible that you can make gains as a result. Keep up with local news and views and get involved in some community-based events around now.

18 FRIDAY ☿   *Moon Age Day 26   Moon Sign Cancer*

There is a great desire within you now to broaden your experience and this is a great month to do it. Travel is likely to be uppermost in your mind and you are keen to learn more about a particular subject. Anything that feeds your intellect is likely to be more than welcome under prevailing planetary trends.

19 SATURDAY   ☿   *Moon Age Day 27   Moon Sign Cancer*

The peak in personal relationships that has been making itself known during the last few days is likely to continue now. You respond positively to people who you haven't cared for in the past, probably because you recognise a change in their attitude. Your responses today are what count the most.

20 SUNDAY   ☿   *Moon Age Day 28   Moon Sign Leo*

This may turn out to be a time for analysing your dreams and for making some of your wishes into hard and fast reality. You will not be inclined to idle away your time, even though you can be quite pensive. Rather you will compartmentalise your day so that there is time for contemplation and hours when you will be extremely busy.

21 MONDAY   ☿   *Moon Age Day 29   Moon Sign Leo*

Travel and new environs interest you right now and there is likely to be a thrust towards excitement as the week gets started. No matter how old you are it is unlikely that you will have lost your sense of wonder when you see something amazing for the first time and now is the chance to put that to the test.

22 TUESDAY   ☿   *Moon Age Day 0   Moon Sign Virgo*

You could easily find that you are luckier than you thought now that the lunar high has arrived. It's time to put your good fortune and your talents to the test and you have the confidence you need to do so. The most satisfying part of today should be the reaction you get from others – especially in a romantic sense.

23 WEDNESDAY ☿   *Moon Age Day 1   Moon Sign Virgo*

Mixing work and leisure is more than possible today and what's more you are getting a lot from some situations that might have seemed dead in the water for the last couple of weeks. The wind of change is blowing through your life and you respond very positively to new input and to exciting suggestions regarding the future.

24 THURSDAY   ☿   *Moon Age Day 2   Moon Sign Virgo*

Take a different and more stimulating approach to old situations today. Friendships are always important to you, though in the main you stick to people you know well. Whilst this continues you are also approaching a fresh and liberating phase when a new series of friends may enter your social circle.

25 FRIDAY ☿   *Moon Age Day 3   Moon Sign Libra*

Today is good for social matters but slightly less effective when it comes to hard work. The simple fact is that you would rather be doing something else, in the company of people you find either stimulating or physically appealing. Romance is on the cards for some, whilst other Virgoans will be strengthening family ties.

26 SATURDAY ☿   *Moon Age Day 4   Moon Sign Libra*

If you work at the weekend stand by to make significant headway – whilst if this is a day off for you there will be a chance to start something new and exciting. Whether or not you agree to co-operate with others in some scheme or other depends on your assessment of the situation. You are definitely a cool cookie at the moment.

27 SUNDAY ☿   *Moon Age Day 5   Moon Sign Scorpio*

Various emotional responses are at work within you now and they could slightly conflict with each other as the day advances. Avoid getting too deep or too serious about anything at all and instead of mulling things over, try a little spontaneity. This isn't usually your way but if it works don't knock it.

28 MONDAY ☿   *Moon Age Day 6   Moon Sign Scorpio*

Emotional support is around when you need it the most, though you may have to seek out the right person to listen to what you have to say. There are likely to be slight disappointments around at the moment but the way you deal with them reveals your progressive mood. Use today to please those you love.

29 TUESDAY ☿   *Moon Age Day 7   Moon Sign Sagittarius*

The time is now clearly right to follow your heart, especially when it comes to relationships. It is towards freedom that you set your sights and a late holiday is certainly not out of the question for many Virgos now. Anything that widens your horizons is likely to appeal to you greatly at this stage.

30 WEDNESDAY ☿   *Moon Age Day 8   Moon Sign Sagittarius*

There are some limitations to face today but you won't allow these to get in your way much. Keep up recent efforts to get to know others better and when it is necessary force yourself to communicate more. Some efforts may seem fraught with difficulty but you are likely to keep moving forward all the same.

31 THURSDAY ☿   *Moon Age Day 9   Moon Sign Sagittarius*

It is towards family and domestic issues that your mind is now inclined to turn, though not in any negative or quiet sense. You want to engage those closest to you in your most cherished schemes and plans – perhaps even if they don't want to be involved at all. Just make sure you remain interesting and, if possible, topical.

September

2017

YOUR MONTH AT A GLANCE

⊕ = Opportunities are around   ⊖ = Be on the defensive   ⬤ = Life is pretty ordinary

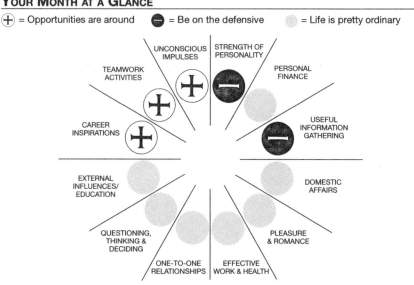

- UNCONSCIOUS IMPULSES
- STRENGTH OF PERSONALITY
- TEAMWORK ACTIVITIES
- PERSONAL FINANCE
- CAREER INSPIRATIONS
- USEFUL INFORMATION GATHERING
- EXTERNAL INFLUENCES/ EDUCATION
- DOMESTIC AFFAIRS
- QUESTIONING, THINKING & DECIDING
- PLEASURE & ROMANCE
- ONE-TO-ONE RELATIONSHIPS
- EFFECTIVE WORK & HEALTH

SEPTEMBER HIGHS AND LOWS

Here I show you how the rhythms of the Moon will affect you this month. Like the tide, your energies and abilities will rise and fall with its pattern. When it is above the centre line, go for it, when it is below, you should be resting.

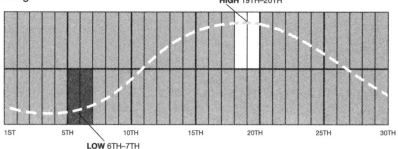

HIGH 19TH–20TH

1ST   5TH   10TH   15TH   20TH   25TH   30TH

LOW 6TH–7TH

1 FRIDAY ☿ *Moon Age Day 10   Moon Sign Capricorn*

You won't have as many hours as you might wish for your home life at the moment and that can be something of a problem at a time when people there have an especially great need of you. You may have to be prepared to restructure your day a little or else postpone or cancel a social event in order to spend time with loved ones.

2 SATURDAY ☿ *Moon Age Day 11   Moon Sign Capricorn*

You remain determined to follow your own path, no matter what the consequences might be. Young or young-at-heart Virgos can be especially entertaining to have around under present planetary trends and you can also find yourself getting into one or two scrapes when in company. Practicality seems to be out of the window.

3 SUNDAY ☿ *Moon Age Day 12   Moon Sign Aquarius*

It is towards the intellectual aspects of life that you tend to be drawn now and across the coming days. You won't be in the least impressed by anything sordid or vulgar and you may even show yourself to be more artistic than is generally the case. You can also impress others with your knowledge.

4 MONDAY ☿ *Moon Age Day 13   Moon Sign Aquarius*

You enjoy the trust and confidence of others – even people who you haven't seen eye-to-eye with in the past. That proves to be very useful because you have big plans right now and cannot go it alone. Romance looks particularly good under present trends and you can find new ways to tell someone how important they are to you.

5 TUESDAY ☿ *Moon Age Day 14   Moon Sign Aquarius*

Although your self-expression might be somewhat inhibited today you are still sure of yourself. The only slight problem is that you don't know how to get your point across to others. Keep in touch with relatives and friends who are presently at a distance and deal with all letters, emails and text messages promptly on this particular Tuesday.

6 WEDNESDAY ☿ *Moon Age Day 15   Moon Sign Pisces*

Don't be too quick to get involved today and remember that with the Moon in the zodiac sign of Pisces you are in the midst of the lunar low. If you are modest in your expectations, all should be well and you will hardly notice this interlude at all. It's only when you expect too much of yourself that things start to go wrong.

7 THURSDAY ☿ *Moon Age Day 16   Moon Sign Pisces*

This is definitely not a good time to be signing any sort of document that will tie you into months or years of commitment. All you have to do to be certain that you are taking the right step is to wait a day or two. In the meantime you seem to be quite intuitive at present and should listen to what your inner voice is telling you.

8 FRIDAY ☿ *Moon Age Day 17   Moon Sign Aries*

It's time to get down to brass tacks and to tell someone the way it really is. This is fine in theory but when you are faced with specific issues you could tend to clam up. It is likely that you will be dealing with people you know well, and who are quite familiar with you. Even though it's difficult you need to speak your mind.

9 SATURDAY ☿ *Moon Age Day 18   Moon Sign Aries*

Don't be too slow to grab an opportunity as soon as it comes along. There are occasions today when you won't get a second chance so it is important to move quickly and to be decisive in your choices. Friends remain helpful and on hand, though most of your real efforts today are likely to be practical or professional.

10 SUNDAY ☿ *Moon Age Day 19   Moon Sign Taurus*

You can find reserves of energy, even when too much is being expected of you. All the same, make it plain to others – even superiors – that you are not a machine and that even Virgo has its limits. You should also spend at least part of today doing something that is purely for fun and which has no practical application at all.

11 MONDAY ☿ *Moon Age Day 20   Moon Sign Taurus*

Today you get a lot from relationships and from personal attachments especially. In a romantic sense you will be extremely attentive and will know instinctively how to bring out the best in your partner. If you expect the whole world to love you at the moment you could be disappointed but most people do and that's what counts.

12 TUESDAY ☿ *Moon Age Day 21   Moon Sign Gemini*

Look out for unexpected delays and unforced errors on your part. Yours is an especially careful nature and this trait turns out to be your best friend right now. If you go out shopping there are bargains to be found, though probably not in the first store you enter. Persistence works well today and you have plenty of that commodity.

13 WEDNESDAY
Moon Age Day 22   Moon Sign Gemini

Today is likely to be very productive, even if it doesn't turn out to be especially exciting. Your capable nature is on display most of the time and you are making a good impression on some potentially important people. Even if life seems dull at the moment you can be certain that there are positive undertones.

14 THURSDAY
Moon Age Day 23   Moon Sign Cancer

Thursday brings the chance to chase your objectives wherever they take you. Don't have too many expectations today because changes of direction are necessary and you must be prepared to take them. Virgo now needs to be at its most flexible and you should also be willing to share and co-operate.

15 FRIDAY
Moon Age Day 24   Moon Sign Cancer

Share your ideas with the world or if that isn't possible at least mention them to one important person. Keeping things bottled up is not the way forward under present trends and neither should you pretend to be less intelligent or shrewd that you really are. Get your detective head on when it comes to solving a mystery.

16 SATURDAY
Moon Age Day 25   Moon Sign Cancer

You should now be enjoying a light-hearted, freewheeling phase and you are unlikely to be taking life very seriously. Get out as much as you can and spend time in the company of people you find diverting and fun to be with. There are new ways to please your partner and maybe a chance to step up the pace of romance.

17 SUNDAY
Moon Age Day 26   Moon Sign Leo

It seems as though everyone around you now has something to say – and all at the same time! Treat this as a significant opportunity to learn new things. Of course not everything that is being said around you is memorable or useful but some parts of it will be. All you have to do today is sort out the wheat from the chaff.

18 MONDAY
Moon Age Day 27   Moon Sign Leo

Superiors and those higher up the promotion tree than you are should be looking at you very favourably right now. If, on the other hand you are between jobs at the moment now would be a really good time to keep your eyes open. There can certainly be professional progress under present trends and social advancement is also possible.

19 TUESDAY
Moon Age Day 28   Moon Sign Virgo

With the lunar high now in attendance you will have very little trouble getting others onside with your ideas or ringing the changes regarding your own life. Socially speaking you are absolutely in the groove and it ought to be a piece of cake to impress almost anyone you choose. There may also be more money about today.

20 WEDNESDAY
Moon Age Day 0   Moon Sign Virgo

Don't wait to be asked at this time but launch yourself into something that really takes your fancy. It looks as though you are going to be dealing with important plans, whilst at the same time showing your most personable side to the world. It's never been easier to get the right kind of support. People are queuing up to help you out.

21 THURSDAY
Moon Age Day 1   Moon Sign Libra

You may not appreciate the methods that someone else is using but you probably cannot deny that they do work. In the main you are likely to follow your own path but if there is something to learn, now is the time to be paying attention. Your partner could be quite demanding at present but there are probably good reasons why.

22 FRIDAY
Moon Age Day 2   Moon Sign Libra

Heady talks and debates of almost any sort are likely to be going well for you around now. You can make a very good impression on others and the fact that you are so willing to take new things on board will not go unnoticed in the right circles. In a social sense you may be quieter than usual but that is likely to change very quickly.

23 SATURDAY
Moon Age Day 3   Moon Sign Scorpio

You should be on tiptop form in the intellectual stakes. If there are quizzes to be entered now is the time to get cracking. It seems you are an expert on everything but the truth is that you have a good all-round general knowledge. People may marvel at the conclusions you reach but there is still an element of good luck involved.

24 SUNDAY
Moon Age Day 4   Moon Sign Scorpio

A new trend comes along that has a very positive bearing on communication – especially when you are talking to people who have influence. You should be confident in your approach and happy to chat casually with anyone. Inspiring new information is likely to come from the least expected directions.

25 MONDAY
Moon Age Day 5   Moon Sign Scorpio

Friendships are positively highlighted, though these tend to be those of long standing. You aren't quite as keen to mix with newcomers or people you don't know at all and even in a social sense you will be happiest with your usual routines. The more progressive qualities within your nature seem to be taking a short break now.

26 TUESDAY
Moon Age Day 6   Moon Sign Sagittarius

You will find that the way ahead is clear in terms of new personal initiatives and success follows on from your efficient way of dealing with life. General good luck is likely to be on your side and you can mix freely with individuals who have it in their power to help you out in some way. You should be much more sociable now.

27 WEDNESDAY
Moon Age Day 7   Moon Sign Sagittarius

This should prove to be a very favourable time for new initiatives. You can capitalise on new ventures and make financial gains as a result of them. When it comes to putting in hard work you are always there and it is because you keep going when others would quit that you succeed in the end. Memories of the past may flood in.

28 THURSDAY
Moon Age Day 8   Moon Sign Capricorn

You will be at your best around now when you are in the company of good friends. Dealing with strangers may not be quite as easy as it was and you could be somewhat suspicious – occasionally without just cause. With the Moon in its present position you will be drawn towards your home life more than towards business.

29 FRIDAY
Moon Age Day 9   Moon Sign Capricorn

If you encounter challenging issues today you will most likely want to defer any decisions until a later date. Co-operation is needed with people who are in the know but even that effort is likely to be sidestepped if possible. By the end of the day things should be looking more positive and Friday evening could even prove to be fun.

30 SATURDAY
Moon Age Day 10   Moon Sign Capricorn

This would be a good day to make changes at home and also for doing things that will please family members. It could be that there is something you have been promising that hasn't come to fruition yet and today would be a great time to address it. Staying on the right side of those you live with is never a bad idea.

October 2017

YOUR MONTH AT A GLANCE

⊕ = Opportunities are around   ⊖ = Be on the defensive   ◯ = Life is pretty ordinary

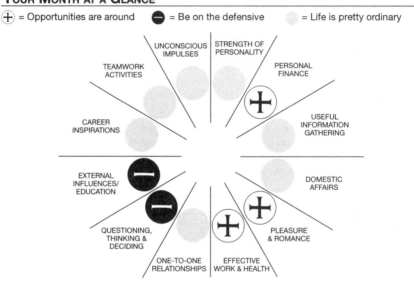

UNCONSCIOUS IMPULSES

STRENGTH OF PERSONALITY

TEAMWORK ACTIVITIES

PERSONAL FINANCE

CAREER INSPIRATIONS

USEFUL INFORMATION GATHERING

EXTERNAL INFLUENCES/ EDUCATION

DOMESTIC AFFAIRS

QUESTIONING, THINKING & DECIDING

PLEASURE & ROMANCE

ONE-TO-ONE RELATIONSHIPS

EFFECTIVE WORK & HEALTH

OCTOBER HIGHS AND LOWS

Here I show you how the rhythms of the Moon will affect you this month. Like the tide, your energies and abilities will rise and fall with its pattern. When it is above the centre line, go for it, when it is below, you should be resting.

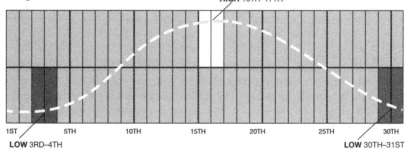

HIGH 16TH–17TH

1ST   5TH   10TH   15TH   20TH   25TH   30TH

LOW 3RD–4TH

LOW 30TH–31ST

104

1 SUNDAY
Moon Age Day 11   Moon Sign Aquarius

Not everyone will be on the same wavelength as you are right now and you may have to modify your stance on a number of different issues in order to accommodate others. You could also be facing a puzzle or two today and will have to think long and hard in order to discover the answers you are seeking.

2 MONDAY
Moon Age Day 12   Moon Sign Aquarius

If you need technical assistance today you should not be afraid to ask for it. Even though you are good at most things there are certain jobs that are best left to experts. In a personal sense it looks as though Virgo is brushing off the odd cobweb and dusting down relationships ahead of a much more progressive romantic phase.

3 TUESDAY
Moon Age Day 13   Moon Sign Pisces

This won't turn out to be the most progressive period you have experienced for some time; in fact you may as well stay in bed for all the impact you are going to make on the world at large. This is not to suggest that there are no gains to be made, simply that you shouldn't expect to move any mountains right now.

4 WEDNESDAY
Moon Age Day 14   Moon Sign Pisces

The great thing about the lunar low this month is that although you won't be taking the world by storm, you don't care whether you do or not. Even for hard-working Virgoans there are moments when you need to sit back and take stock. Now is such an interlude and you should relish the opportunity to be more of a watcher.

5 THURSDAY
Moon Age Day 15   Moon Sign Aries

It would be very easy to be distracted today, for example by gossip. Although you will be quite interested to hear the comments from those around you today you should also be wise enough to make up your own mind about all situations. Experience counts for a great deal when you are dealing with professional matters.

6 FRIDAY
Moon Age Day 16   Moon Sign Aries

Be very sure of yourself today before you proceed down any unknown and slightly scary path. This is as true in your social life as it is in a professional sense and you will probably relish the company and support of people you know and trust. For once the recently courageous Virgo is just a little apprehensive.

7 SATURDAY
Moon Age Day 17   Moon Sign Taurus

Standing up for your rights might be slightly more difficult today, mostly because you may not be entirely sure what they are. That's why it is most important to do a little research, to ask the right questions and to read the correct documents. Only when you know the facts of a situation can you move forward and sort it out.

8 SUNDAY
Moon Age Day 18   Moon Sign Taurus

There are significant signs that you are about to undergo a great many changes, though most of these have to do with the way you think and not necessarily with the way you live or work. Virgo begins to open up and to be more honest with itself as well as with other people. Such a metamorphosis can be somewhat uncomfortable.

9 MONDAY
Moon Age Day 19   Moon Sign Taurus

How very jolly you are likely to feel at the moment and just how much happiness you can bring into the lives of those you deal with in a moment-by-moment sense. With more money likely to be coming your way in the near future it looks as though all your hard work in the recent past is now beginning to pay off quite handsomely.

10 TUESDAY
Moon Age Day 20   Moon Sign Gemini

You put on a bold face to the world, even if you are not half as confident as you appear to be. Don't play silly games with people over issues that are far too important to treat lightly and make sure your lover knows exactly how you feel about things. It may be time for a fairly serious heart-to-heart talk.

11 WEDNESDAY
Moon Age Day 21   Moon Sign Gemini

So good is your intuition right now that you won't have any trouble at all working out whether someone is trustworthy or not. The only difficulty could be in convincing others that you are correct. It might eventually be necessary to allow those around you to formulate their own conclusions, whilst you rely heavily on your own gut feelings.

12 THURSDAY
Moon Age Day 22   Moon Sign Cancer

Cool, calm and collected – that's the way Virgo is likely to be just at present. You won't want to push yourself too hard, though you find some interesting shortcuts to success – ones of a sort that wouldn't normally appeal to you. If ever there was a zodiac sign that is ultimately capable of going the long way round it is Virgo.

13 FRIDAY
Moon Age Day 23   Moon Sign Cancer

In most cases if you can visualise it, you can do it. This isn't exclusively true at the moment but when it matters the most your imagination can be a great assistant. Don't get so tied down with Virgo routines that you fail to engage your more dreamy side on occasions. Reach out for something you really want and touch it in your mind.

14 SATURDAY
Moon Age Day 24   Moon Sign Leo

If there is one thing about your nature that almost always remains the same it is your very practical approach to most situations. This can be a tremendous boon to you at present because people around you, especially if you are at work, simply don't have your flair for getting it right first time. Your mechanical skills are particularly good now.

15 SUNDAY
Moon Age Day 25   Moon Sign Leo

It is going to be the personal side of your life that brings out the very best in you this Sunday and you should be keen to find new things to do. You relish the company of people you really like and won't be too keen to mix with strangers or even acquaintances for the moment. This is about to change.

16 MONDAY
Moon Age Day 26   Moon Sign Virgo

The real boost today doesn't so much come from the direction of the lunar high but rather from a mixture of determination and staying power, both of which are well marked at the moment. Very little would cause you to divert from a path you have deliberately and carefully chosen and as is often the case, success is the result.

17 TUESDAY
Moon Age Day 27   Moon Sign Virgo

You can now afford to take a few more chances, though whether you will or not remains to be seen because it isn't your way to gamble too much. Money may come from fairly unexpected sources and you could find yourself significantly better off than you might have expected at this time of the month.

18 WEDNESDAY
Moon Age Day 28   Moon Sign Libra

Today you have a good sense of fun but also perhaps a tendency to act on emotional impulses rather on sound common sense. This won't please you much because as an Earth sign you love to be fully in command of yourself. On the other hand this is something of a holiday for Virgo and perhaps should be treated as such.

19 THURSDAY
Moon Age Day 29   Moon Sign Libra

Career developments are likely to see you with a heightened sense of self-confidence and optimism. It becomes apparent that you are now in the driving seat and that you have what it takes to convince those around you to follow your lead. In a romantic sense especially you are now fully in charge.

20 FRIDAY
Moon Age Day 0   Moon Sign Libra

You might now be inclined to give way to a little mental restlessness but this is a situation you can counter by getting something different and interesting into your life at every possible opportunity. It would be all too easy to get bored or to settle for what you know because it's comfortable. Some effort is necessary but the rewards are great.

21 SATURDAY
Moon Age Day 1   Moon Sign Scorpio

If you feel slightly bored today and in need of a change of scene, do try to avoid being over-impulsive. There are ways and means to make yourself feel more content with your lot and you don't have to turn your entire life upside down. By this evening you will be ready to enjoy your social life.

22 SUNDAY
Moon Age Day 2   Moon Sign Scorpio

Although you are clearly fired up by ambition and should do everything you can to take positive steps towards your dreams, you also need to leave time aside for simple relaxation. At social occasions you should prove to be a hit but you may find yourself associating with people who drive you up the wall.

23 MONDAY
Moon Age Day 3   Moon Sign Sagittarius

The start of a new working week is likely to find you busy and filled with enterprise. Seek out like-minded people because you are especially co-operative now and can formulate successful and long-lasting partnerships. As far as your home life is concerned you might be somewhat agitated by the behaviour of younger people.

24 TUESDAY
Moon Age Day 4   Moon Sign Sagittarius

There are some very subtle influences around at this time so be thoughtful and alert to the nuances of your mood. You may not get quite as much done as you would wish in a concrete sense but your ability to sort things out in your mind has rarely been better. Routines may seem quite comforting at this stage.

25 WEDNESDAY   *Moon Age Day 5   Moon Sign Sagittarius*

In a professional sense it looks as though you will now be able to reap the benefit of all the effort you have been putting in recently. You are certainly likely to be on form and your ideas are interesting to almost anyone who learns about them. One particularly ingenious plan could streamline an otherwise tedious process.

26 THURSDAY   *Moon Age Day 6   Moon Sign Capricorn*

Your social life is likely to be happy and stimulating at this time. You tend to meet interesting and dynamic people and you have much to offer. Don't allow your idea of your own limitations to hold you back in any situation or let your natural modesty get in the way of a very big idea. You have an eye for the main chance and should also be lucky now.

27 FRIDAY   *Moon Age Day 7   Moon Sign Capricorn*

This is a time when you need to gain approval, not because you doubt your own reasoning but merely for the sake of your own self-esteem. In a way it is a low-key way of blowing your own trumpet, but there is nothing at all wrong with that. People should be pleased to confirm your conclusions and will find you warm and friendly.

28 SATURDAY   *Moon Age Day 8   Moon Sign Aquarius*

Your social life is likely to expand this weekend and although it is relatively easy for you to get things done in a practical sense it is more likely that you will be drawn into having fun. This would be a good time in which to broaden your experiences through travel but if you don't have the time to go wandering physically, you can do so in your head.

29 SUNDAY   *Moon Age Day 9   Moon Sign Aquarius*

Peace and quiet at home probably won't be much of an option today. It will seem as though there is always some situation or another that is demanding your attention and there could also be a great deal of noise and commotion around. As a result you might decide it would be better to go somewhere else, though the noise will probably go with you.

30 MONDAY   *Moon Age Day 10   Moon Sign Pisces*

Life could so easily turn out to be a series of misunderstandings whilst the lunar low is around and if you want to avoid these you are going to have to explain yourself carefully on numerous occasions. All of this holds you up slightly and can be quite frustrating but forewarned is forearmed and arguments can be circumvented.

31 TUESDAY
Moon Age Day 11   Moon Sign Pisces

Whatever you take on board today, be aware that your level of energy is not high and that common good luck doesn't really favour your efforts now. For these reasons it might be best to watch and wait while you allow others to make most of the running. At least personal attachments should be unaffected by the lunar low.

$\mathfrak{M}$ November 2017

YOUR MONTH AT A GLANCE

(+) = Opportunities are around   ● = Be on the defensive   ◯ = Life is pretty ordinary

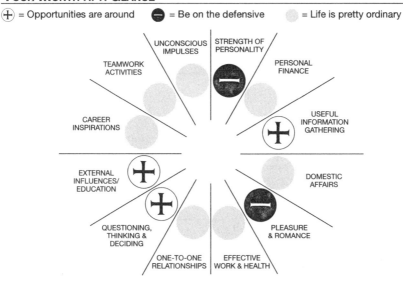

UNCONSCIOUS IMPULSES

STRENGTH OF PERSONALITY

TEAMWORK ACTIVITIES

PERSONAL FINANCE

CAREER INSPIRATIONS

USEFUL INFORMATION GATHERING

EXTERNAL INFLUENCES/ EDUCATION

DOMESTIC AFFAIRS

QUESTIONING, THINKING & DECIDING

PLEASURE & ROMANCE

ONE-TO-ONE RELATIONSHIPS

EFFECTIVE WORK & HEALTH

NOVEMBER HIGHS AND LOWS

Here I show you how the rhythms of the Moon will affect you this month. Like the tide, your energies and abilities will rise and fall with its pattern. When it is above the centre line, go for it, when it is below, you should be resting.

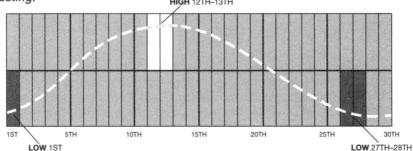

HIGH 12TH–13TH

1ST   5TH   10TH   15TH   20TH   25TH   30TH

LOW 1ST

LOW 27TH–28TH

1 WEDNESDAY
Moon Age Day 12   Moon Sign Pisces

You may discover that you are now more ambitious, probably because of events that have taken place across the last week or so. A position that you never expected to hold could well be in the offing and general trends show that you begin to have more confidence in your ability to get ahead in life than has been the case for a while.

2 THURSDAY
Moon Age Day 13   Moon Sign Aries

Professional success is likely to come naturally, even if you find yourself fending off individuals who are extremely competitive. You make your way forward slowly, steadily and with great panache, whereas those around you are more likely to struggle. People will admire your cool and efficient way of getting things done.

3 FRIDAY
Moon Age Day 14   Moon Sign Aries

Wherever practical initiatives are concerned you may find information relating to projects that are becoming ever more important to you. This is a time to lead from the front and to convince others that you really know what you are talking about. Expect some good results from your efforts and enlist the support of colleagues.

4 SATURDAY
Moon Age Day 15   Moon Sign Taurus

It is probably not a good idea to believe everything you hear today. For one thing your informants have probably got hold of the wrong end of the stick and for another they may have a vested interest in telling a tale in a particular way. It would be better by far to receive a couple of unbiased accounts and then to make up your own mind.

5 SUNDAY
Moon Age Day 16   Moon Sign Taurus

Domestic and family ties benefit from present planetary trends and you will be getting on especially well with younger people. It seems that you are presently very good at putting yourself in the other person's shoes, no matter how different those might be to your own. People appreciate your ability to listen quietly and offer sound advice.

6 MONDAY
Moon Age Day 17   Moon Sign Gemini

You need to allow your personality to shine out today because that's all it takes to impress those around you. Things should be better on the romantic front and that means you may be spending a loving period with that most special person. Some friends can be quite distant today – and not in terms of miles.

7 TUESDAY
Moon Age Day 18   Moon Sign Gemini

Virgo could now be rather too idealistic for its own good. It's fine to have beliefs and to follow them as much as you can but there are moments when a greater degree of flexibility proves to be necessary in the real world. You have to remember that not everyone's values and opinions are going to be the same as yours.

8 WEDNESDAY
Moon Age Day 19   Moon Sign Cancer

Although practical matters can prove to be quite tiresome today you do realise that they have to be dealt with and nobody is better at addressing them than you are. More imagination could be called for later in the day and it looks as though you are going to have to be very flexible in your dealings with errant family members.

9 THURSDAY
Moon Age Day 20   Moon Sign Cancer

Although there are likely to be some misunderstandings to deal with today, in the main you manage to sort these out quite easily and won't be held up much by anything. You see your way forward quite clearly and though you may not be taking too many practical steps today your mind is set on positive actions for later.

10 FRIDAY
Moon Age Day 21   Moon Sign Leo

It looks as though you will become assertive and even forceful for the moment. That's fine just as long as you don't allow things to get out of hand. A little humility along the way is also important, if only because it shows other people that you are keeping your feet on the ground. New friendships are likely around now.

11 SATURDAY
Moon Age Day 22   Moon Sign Leo

Being in the know can make a big difference when it comes to achieving successes and that is why it would be most sensible to keep your ear to the ground today. Even the most casual remarks can offer you invaluable clues and once you take these on board you are half way to achieving some notable coups, especially at work.

12 SUNDAY
Moon Age Day 23   Moon Sign Virgo

There is now a real emphasis on making money and you will be doing all you can to increase the amount coming into your purse or pocket. With some very ingenious ideas at your disposal you should also be in a good position to work out strategies for the future, even years ahead, that will keep the cash rolling in.

13 MONDAY
Moon Age Day 24   Moon Sign Virgo

You show a very cheerful and tolerant attitude towards almost everyone and will be popular, as much for what you are giving out as for any other reason. Virgo can be a quiet sign sometimes but that doesn't appear to be the case at present because you seem to be the life and soul of the party.

14 TUESDAY
Moon Age Day 25   Moon Sign Libra

This is a marvellous time to reaffirm your identity and to make sure that everyone knows who you are and what you want. In fact you can be a variety of different individuals today, dependent on what you are doing. In each case it is important to show yourself in the best possible light to the maximum number of people.

15 WEDNESDAY
Moon Age Day 26   Moon Sign Libra

Virgo is normally very careful and that certainly seems to be true today. No matter how much other people push you will only do what seems right and sensible to you personally. In the main that's fine because your friends know you well but you may have to make a few exceptions in the case of new acquaintances or strangers.

16 THURSDAY
Moon Age Day 27   Moon Sign Libra

You will now be more gregarious and extremely generous to those you care about. To counter this somewhat you won't be inclined to give anything away to people you don't know or who you find difficult to trust. Virgo can be very partisan on occasions and this is now more likely than ever. Details matter to you at this time.

17 FRIDAY
Moon Age Day 28   Moon Sign Scorpio

It is clear that you will benefit from being out of doors and in places with wide horizons. Your confidence remains generally high but there may be moments when you are more inclined to doubt yourself, especially if things start to go wrong. Keep faith with your original opinions and methods and don't change horses in midstream.

18 SATURDAY
Moon Age Day 0   Moon Sign Scorpio

Don't take too many risks this weekend and if you are regularly involved in sporting activities you need to be especially careful for the moment. It isn't that anything is likely to go very wrong but you are not quite as co-ordinated as you usually are. People generally are likely to seem duller than usual – or is that your own attitude?

19 SUNDAY
Moon Age Day 1   Moon Sign Sagittarius

You can rid your life of a few nonessentials now and start some new trends. Get together with a trusted individual and start working on new strategies that have been playing around in your head for a while. There are some gains to be made today from showing how inspirational you can be, particularly when it comes to romance.

20 MONDAY
Moon Age Day 2   Moon Sign Sagittarius

If there are problems regarding joint finances around now you need to sit down and talk things through, rather than keeping silent and hoping everything will come good in the end. It might also be sensible to reassess your attachments to certain possessions. Are you benefiting from them or working just to maintain them?

21 TUESDAY
Moon Age Day 3   Moon Sign Sagittarius

You should fit quite well into almost any slot today and that is because you are making yourself so adaptable. It doesn't matter much what company you keep because you change like a chameleon in order to suit your environment – a fact that isn't lost on those around you. In romance you are considerate, caring and, in the eyes of someone, sexy.

22 WEDNESDAY
Moon Age Day 4   Moon Sign Capricorn

You tend to personify self-sacrifice today because you will go so far in order to make those around you happy. To do so will seem more important than feathering your own nest, though if you are wise you can achieve both objectives at the same time. You may be adopting a new attitude with regard to family matters.

23 THURSDAY
Moon Age Day 5   Moon Sign Capricorn

You now begin to develop a deeply analytical approach to quite a few matters, which is typical of Virgo. Your practical skills are certainly on display and you may be able to sort out a mess caused by others. There is no doubt that you are the right person to call upon for assistance. Watch how many people realise this.

24 FRIDAY
Moon Age Day 6   Moon Sign Aquarius

Given the right social circumstances and a responsive crowd you can give a good account of yourself at the moment, even if the underlying trend is for you to be fairly quiet for most of the time. You have a strong need for reassurance, especially in your work, and you won't approach anything new unless you are very sure of yourself.

25 SATURDAY
Moon Age Day 7   Moon Sign Aquarius

A wonderful boost to your social life comes along now and the weekend ought to work out somewhat better than you may have expected. This is because you are in the mood to entertain and also on account of the sort of people who are gathering around you at this time. Today is not a period for working too hard or for worrying.

26 SUNDAY
Moon Age Day 8   Moon Sign Aquarius

Someone is likely to challenge you today, or else make statements with which you definitely do not agree. Whether or not you do anything about the situation depends on how strongly you feel about it. The chances are that for the moment you will keep your counsel. But heaven help anyone who crosses you in any way tomorrow.

27 MONDAY
Moon Age Day 9   Moon Sign Pisces

Whatever you decide is right for today – go for it Virgo. Don't let anyone tell you what you should be thinking or doing and use the lunar high to the best of your ability in every practical sense. This is not the sort of day to wait in a queue or to stand around wondering whether you should move or not. Keep friends laughing all day.

28 TUESDAY
Moon Age Day 10   Moon Sign Pisces

Another good day is in store, though today probably won't be quite as eventful as yesterday. What the lunar high leaves you right now is a strong sense of purpose, a desire to enjoy yourself and a great deal of affection for those around you. All of these are positive ingredients for a Tuesday that can be filled with joy and happiness.

29 WEDNESDAY
Moon Age Day 11   Moon Sign Aries

Your natural sensitivity is well emphasised and you tend to be more of a shrinking violet today – unless you are dealing with matters you understand absolutely. Finding the level of confidence you need to make big changes is going to be hard, which is why you tend to nibble away at the edge of things.

30 THURSDAY
Moon Age Day 12   Moon Sign Aries

There is now a possibility that you will express yourself somewhat vaguely and you are unlikely to take sufficient time out to work out what you should be saying. When it matters the most and you are dealing with someone you love deeply, words probably won't be important in any case – a simple look may be enough.

December

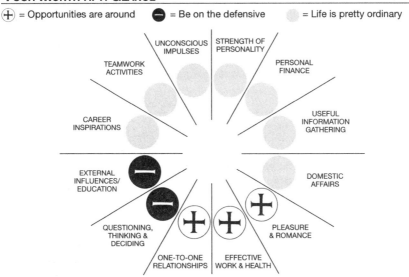

2017

YOUR MONTH AT A GLANCE

⊕ = Opportunities are around   ⊖ = Be on the defensive   ⬤ = Life is pretty ordinary

UNCONSCIOUS IMPULSES

STRENGTH OF PERSONALITY

TEAMWORK ACTIVITIES

PERSONAL FINANCE

CAREER INSPIRATIONS

USEFUL INFORMATION GATHERING

EXTERNAL INFLUENCES/ EDUCATION

DOMESTIC AFFAIRS

QUESTIONING, THINKING & DECIDING

PLEASURE & ROMANCE

ONE-TO-ONE RELATIONSHIPS

EFFECTIVE WORK & HEALTH

DECEMBER HIGHS AND LOWS

Here I show you how the rhythms of the Moon will affect you this month. Like the tide, your energies and abilities will rise and fall with its pattern. When it is above the centre line, go for it, when it is below, you should be resting.

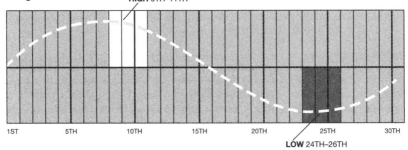

HIGH 9TH–11TH

1ST   5TH   10TH   15TH   20TH   25TH   30TH

LOW 24TH–26TH

1 FRIDAY
Moon Age Day 13   Moon Sign Taurus

It's almost as if you can fly at present because you seem to have a bird's eye view of life. You can see when people are doing things badly – or when they are not doing them at all, and you know very well when people could do with a hand. Once you have such an understanding it ought to be simple to lend a timely helping hand.

2 SATURDAY
Moon Age Day 14   Moon Sign Taurus

Being part of a team is likely to work out for the best for you today. Although you are quite single-minded as a rule you will now have a greater willingness to see another point of view, even when it is radically different from your own. Somewhere there is someone who could be of great help to you today. Your job is to find out just who it is.

3 SUNDAY   ☿
Moon Age Day 15   Moon Sign Gemini

Your sensitivity increases and you are apt to be in a fairly dreamy state. This might cause you to think about the past and to become slightly nostalgic. The fact that Christmas is not far ahead won't help this tendency, though of course there is nothing at all wrong with enjoying a few happy memories – perhaps try to share them?

4 MONDAY   ☿
Moon Age Day 16   Moon Sign Gemini

Your love life could put a little strain on matters at the start of this week. Maybe you are just not feeling amorous or it could be that your partner is slightly difficult to deal with at the moment. One way or another you are far more likely to mix freely with a number of different people and to leave the deeper emotions for another day.

5 TUESDAY   ☿
Moon Age Day 17   Moon Sign Cancer

Though personal relationships could be slightly low-key at this stage, you will get on well with just about everyone. You feel the need to share your affection around and may not be in the mood to make a special fuss of any one individual. Some new starts you make today could seem too slow but it won't take you long to gain speed.

6 WEDNESDAY   ☿
Moon Age Day 18   Moon Sign Cancer

You now find yourself more expressive and well able to communicate with just about anyone you come across. Not all your efforts to help others will work out strictly as you might have expected and there could be the odd disappointment on the way. In the main you will be happiest at the moment when the pace of life is extremely fast.

7 THURSDAY ☿ *Moon Age Day 19   Moon Sign Leo*

There are lots of communications to deal with now and also quite possibly a feeling that you would like to spend more time in and around your home. When you are dealing with practical matters it is important to do things your own way and not to get bogged down by the rather strange ideas of others. Virgo usually knows what to do.

8 FRIDAY ☿ *Moon Age Day 20   Moon Sign Leo*

A dilemma of some sort is likely to arise in relationships. Find a balance between acting upon your own personal needs and the requirements that others have of you. If there are any problems today these could arise as a result of a misunderstanding and not for any solid or serious reason. Things can be talked through easily enough.

9 SATURDAY ☿ *Moon Age Day 21   Moon Sign Virgo*

You seem to thrive on a challenge at present and will be facing most situations head on today. There is very little that is now beyond your capabilities and the lunar high also makes you much luckier and inclined to succeed at most things first time. When Virgo is in this frame of mind nobody is inclined to argue.

10 SUNDAY ☿ *Moon Age Day 22   Moon Sign Virgo*

You continue to make things happen, both inside and outside of work. What is also significant is the fact that your popularity is about as high as it can get. That means you are flavour of the month, even to people you don't normally get on with too well. You should also expect to be doing rather well in the financial stakes.

11 MONDAY ☿ *Moon Age Day 23   Moon Sign Virgo*

Your ideas are good and definitely make sense, not only to you but also to colleagues and friends. Don't keep things to yourself, especially when it is something that has been on your mind for weeks. It's time to break the mould as far as Virgo is concerned and to show everyone just how amazing you can be.

12 THURSDAY ☿ *Moon Age Day 24   Moon Sign Libra*

Opportunities come along to improve your lot in and around your home. It should now be easier to listen to relatives who have been having a slightly difficult time and to implement plans that can help. Time stretches like elastic for Virgo at this stage of the week and you will be amazed at just how much you can achieve.

13 WEDNESDAY ☿   *Moon Age Day 25   Moon Sign Libra*

Communication remains especially important and it is within your social interactions that your greatest joys come at the moment. It may be occurring to you for the first time just how close it is to Christmas but being the sort of person you are you won't panic. Rather you will sit down and make a plan for yourself.

14 THURSDAY ☿   *Moon Age Day 26   Moon Sign Scorpio*

You are unlikely to be making snap decisions today but will be thinking things through very carefully indeed. That's your way and though it doesn't always impress other people, you can't avoid this side of your nature. It looks as though you will be showing ever more concern for certain individuals who are worse off than you are.

15 FRIDAY ☿   *Moon Age Day 27   Moon Sign Scorpio*

Money matters can be quite complex to deal with and when they involve your partner or the family as a whole you might decide that a meeting of minds is called for. You are unlikely to take draconian actions of any sort at this time and can be guaranteed to show a fair and even-handed attitude to almost any situation.

16 SATURDAY ☿   *Moon Age Day 28   Moon Sign Scorpio*

Communication with influential people could prove to be worth a good deal to you at this time and it seems as though you come across interesting types all the time. If you are at work you might have to stand up for your rights more than usual – that is if you don't want colleagues to be either stealing your thunder or else using your ideas.

17 SUNDAY ☿   *Moon Age Day 29   Moon Sign Sagittarius*

What a great time this is likely to be for pleasant social relationships. Maybe it's the onset of the festive season but more likely it is the planetary influences that surround you. For whatever reason you become more open and can even make the running in most situations. Don't leave important little details of any sort to chance.

18 MONDAY ☿   *Moon Age Day 0   Moon Sign Sagittarius*

There's no doubt that today works better for you if you concentrate on a specific task rather than trying to get everything done at the same time. There's a bit of a dichotomy today because although you want to have everything straight and logical, rules and regulations are inclined to get on your nerves. Make careful moves.

19 TUESDAY ☿ *Moon Age Day 1 Moon Sign Capricorn*

You like to manifest yourself and your talents in a truly original way and you could also be making use of some of the gifts that come to you at present. This would be a good time to travel, maybe to see family members or friends, though some Virgos could even be utilising this time to take a fantastic holiday.

20 WEDNESDAY ☿ *Moon Age Day 2 Moon Sign Capricorn*

Money, property and possessions will all play an important part in your thinking in this part of December. You see new opportunities picked out as if they were underlined and you can't understand why everyone isn't as dynamic and go-getting as you presently are. Make allowances for a colleague or a friend with real problems.

21 THURSDAY ☿ *Moon Age Day 3 Moon Sign Capricorn*

Circumstances might seem to conspire to irritate you today, especially at work. There are a few troublesome planets about at the moment as far as you are concerned but none are malevolent. Take things in your stride and don't react to circumstances you cannot alter. Later in the day you are likely to feel somewhat less frazzled.

22 FRIDAY ☿ *Moon Age Day 4 Moon Sign Aquarius*

Your real forte now lies in communication, which isn't always the case for Virgo. You will also enjoy anything mentally stimulating and intellectual. If you decide on an outing today it would be good to go somewhere that gets you thinking and creative. Pleasing your lover should be easier now than at any stage.

23 SATURDAY *Moon Age Day 5 Moon Sign Aquarius*

This could be a more relaxing day, though of course it all depends on family commitments because some Virgoans could be up until the early hours wrapping those last-minute presents. In the main you will choose to have fun and can do much to lift the spirits of everyone around you. For once Virgo is a true optimist.

24 SUNDAY *Moon Age Day 6 Moon Sign Pisces*

Today can bring you face-to-face with consequences, especially if you make rash decisions whilst the lunar low is around. It would be far better for the moment to defer making up your mind until you feel more certain of your position. Friends should prove to be very supportive and you may be inclined to rely on them.

25 MONDAY
Moon Age Day 7   Moon Sign Pisces

You may feel a little reluctant to become involved in matters that you would have grasped with both hands last week, but don't panic because this is a very temporary state of affairs. This might be a slightly muted Christmas Day in some respects but you should feel generally safe, secure and very loved.

26 TUESDAY
Moon Age Day 8   Moon Sign Pisces

Getting out and about is more likely from tomorrow on and left to your own devices you might be quite happy to stay around your own fireside for the moment. Of course that might not be possible but do at least try to take part of the day to relax. You also have a growing and quite perceptible desire to solve puzzles of one sort or another.

27 WEDNESDAY
Moon Age Day 9   Moon Sign Aries

If there are obstacles in your path today you need to carry on regardless of them. There are times at the moment when standard responses won't work and that's where your present ingenuity comes in. Get together with people you don't see much during the year and make the most of social encounters to further your own ideas.

28 THURSDAY
Moon Age Day 10   Moon Sign Aries

It would be far too easy right now to come across as somewhat self-centred and although this isn't really the case, try to show a little humility to convince others. Your concern is not simply for yourself but on behalf of those who are important in your life. The only problem could be that they fail to realise it.

29 FRIDAY
Moon Age Day 11   Moon Sign Taurus

Lots of your energy is piled equally into work and play around now and there is a balance to your life that should be pleasing you no end. You are not that far away from completing something that could seem to be a real chore and with the end of one phase will come the potential start of another. It's time to start planning well ahead.

30 SATURDAY
Moon Age Day 12   Moon Sign Taurus

It seems to be your technical know-how that helps you to get on at work or at home and there isn't any doubt that specialist skills are worth most to you today. Concentrate on those things you know that others don't because people are likely to be relying heavily on you. You can shine like a star in all social settings both today and for New Year.

31 SUNDAY   *Moon Age Day 13   Moon Sign Gemini*

This may be the best day of the whole Christmas period for get-togethers and for meeting up with people you really love but who you don't spend time with very often. Whilst others make hopeful resolutions for the year ahead, you remain confident that you have everything in place to ensure your continued success.

How to Calculate Your Rising Sign

Most astrologers agree that, next to the Sun Sign, the most important influence on any person is the Rising Sign at the time of their birth. The Rising Sign represents the astrological sign that was rising over the eastern horizon when each and every one of us came into the world. It is sometimes also called the Ascendant.

Let us suppose, for example, that you were born with the Sun in the zodiac sign of Libra. This would bestow certain characteristics on you that are likely to be shared by all other Librans. However, a Libran with Aries Rising would show a very different attitude towards life, and of course relationships, than a Libran with Pisces Rising.

For these reasons, this book shows how your zodiac Rising Sign has a bearing on all the possible positions of the Sun at birth. Simply look through the Aries table opposite.

As long as you know your approximate time of birth the graph will show you how to discover your Rising Sign.

Look across the top of the graph of your zodiac sign to find your date of birth, and down the side for your birth time (I have used Greenwich Mean Time). Where they cross is your Rising Sign. Don't forget to subtract an hour (or two) if appropriate for Summer Time.

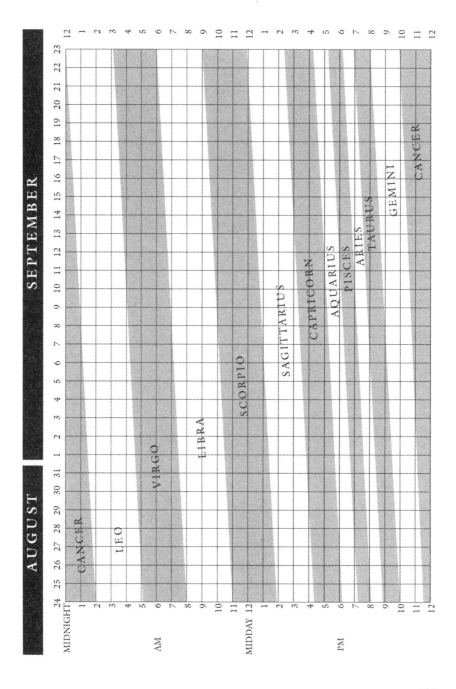

THE ZODIAC, PLANETS AND CORRESPONDENCES

The Earth revolves around the Sun once every calendar year, so when viewed from Earth the Sun appears in a different part of the sky as the year progresses. In astrology, these parts of the sky are divided into the signs of the zodiac and this means that the signs are organised in a circle. The circle begins with Aries and ends with Pisces.

Taking the zodiac sign as a starting point, astrologers then work with all the positions of planets, stars and many other factors to calculate horoscopes and birth charts and tell us what the stars have in store for us.

The table below shows the planets and Elements for each of the signs of the zodiac. Each sign belongs to one of the four Elements: Fire, Air, Earth or Water. Fire signs are creative and enthusiastic; Air signs are mentally active and thoughtful; Earth signs are constructive and practical; Water signs are emotional and have strong feelings.

It also shows the metals and gemstones associated with, or corresponding with, each sign. The correspondence is made when a metal or stone possesses properties that are held in common with a particular sign of the zodiac.

Finally, the table shows the opposite of each star sign – this is the opposite sign in the astrological circle.

Placed	Sign	Symbol	Element	Planet	Metal	Stone	Opposite
1	Aries	Ram	Fire	Mars	Iron	Bloodstone	Libra
2	Taurus	Bull	Earth	Venus	Copper	Sapphire	Scorpio
3	Gemini	Twins	Air	Mercury	Mercury	Tiger's Eye	Sagittarius
4	Cancer	Crab	Water	Moon	Silver	Pearl	Capricorn
5	Leo	Lion	Fire	Sun	Gold	Ruby	Aquarius
6	Virgo	Maiden	Earth	Mercury	Mercury	Sardonyx	Pisces
7	Libra	Scales	Air	Venus	Copper	Sapphire	Aries
8	Scorpio	Scorpion	Water	Pluto	Plutonium	Jasper	Taurus
9	Sagittarius	Archer	Fire	Jupiter	Tin	Topaz	Gemini
10	Capricorn	Goat	Earth	Saturn	Lead	Black Onyx	Cancer
11	Aquarius	Waterbearer	Air	Uranus	Uranium	Amethyst	Leo
12	Pisces	Fishes	Water	Neptune	Tin	Moonstone	Virgo